209, 210, 211, 212, 213, 233

ORGANIC CHEMISTRY 1 LECTURE GUIDE 2019

BY RHETT C. SMITH

Marketed by Proton Guru

Find additional online resources and guides at protonguru.com

Try out *Organic Chemistry 1 Primer*
    and
Organic Chemistry 1 Reaction and Practice Problem Book

For concise, plain-language, study-on-your own organic help and practice

There is a lot of online video content to accompany this book at the Proton Guru YouTube Channel! Just go to YouTube and search "Proton Guru Channel" to easily find our content.

Instructors: Free PowerPoint lecture slides to accompany this text can be obtained by emailing IQ@protonguru.com from your accredited institution email account. The homepage at protonguru.com provides a link to citations to popular text books for further reading on each Lesson topic in this primer.

© 2006-2018

Executive Editor: Rhett C. Smith, Ph.D. You can reach him through our office at: IQ@protonguru.com

All rights reserved. No part of this book may be reproduced or distributed, in any form or by any means, without permission in writing from the Executive Editor. This includes but is not limited to storage or broadcast for online or distance learning courses.

Printed in the United States of America

10 9 8 7 6 5 4 3 2 1

ISBN 978-1074137434

D1296644

Organic Chemistry 1 Lecture Guide 2019

By Rhett C. Smith, Ph.D.

© 2006, 2011-2019

Companion Books from the Proton Guru:

Organic Chemistry 1 Reactions and Practice Problems 2019

by Rhett C. Smith

Organic Chemistry 1 Primer 2019,

by Rhett C. Smith, Andrew G. Tennyson, and Tania Houjeiry

1. Opposite Charges Attract

- stabilizing
- favorable

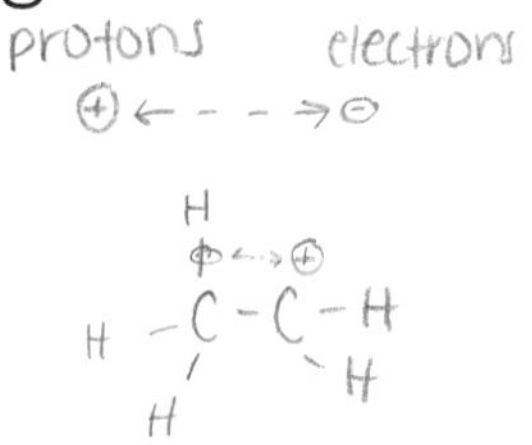

protons   electrons
⊕ ← - - → ⊖

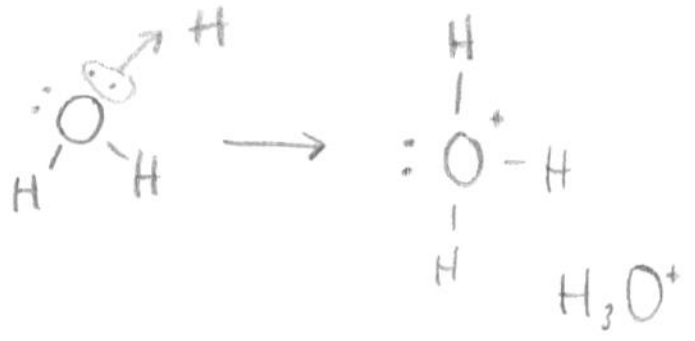

H
⊕ ←→ ⊕
H — C - C — H
    | ` H
    H

H_2O^+

2. Like Charges Repel

- destabilizing
- unfavorable

More Stable

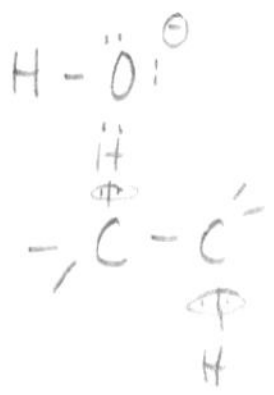

$H - \ddot{O} :^{\ominus}$

less stable

repulsion
H ↓ H
⊕ | ⊕
⁻ C - C ⁻

⁻ C - C ´
         ⊕
         H

H ⊕ C - Ö: repulsion

Notes

When given the formula for a molecule or ion:

1. Add up valence electrons; if it is an ion and has a charge, add an electron for each "−" charge, take away an electron for each "+" charge.

2. Draw single bonds between the atoms

3. Add remaining valence electrons to the atoms to give them the expected number of lone pairs (you know this from the Lewis structure of the given element)

4. Add bonds between adjacent elements that have open valences, making multiple bonds.

HINT:

Most neutral species we will encounter in this class feature elements with a total of 8 electrons (an **octet**) around them in the correct structure, except H, which will have only 2.

Notes

Target	Atoms	#e⁻	Structure
A. CCl_4	C		
	4×Cl		
B. CH_3OH	C		
	4×H		
	O		
C. CH_2O	C		
	2×H		
	O		

Notes

dash formula   condensed formula   bond-line formula

(A)

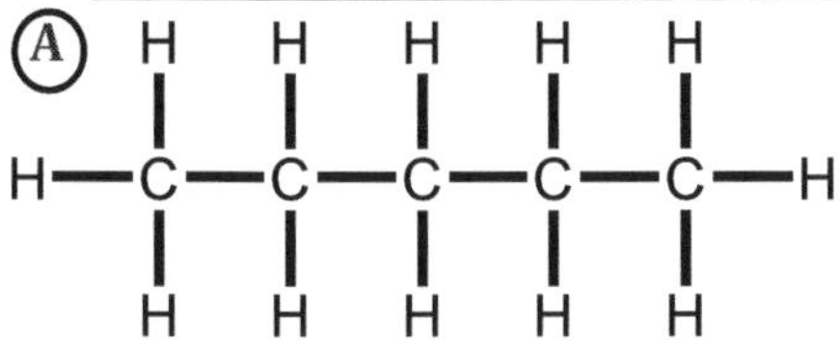

H—C—C—C—C—C—H

$CH_3CH_2CH_2CH_2CH_3$
$CH_3(CH_2)_3CH_3$

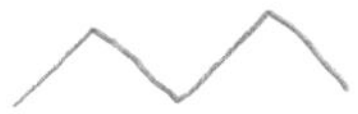

(B)

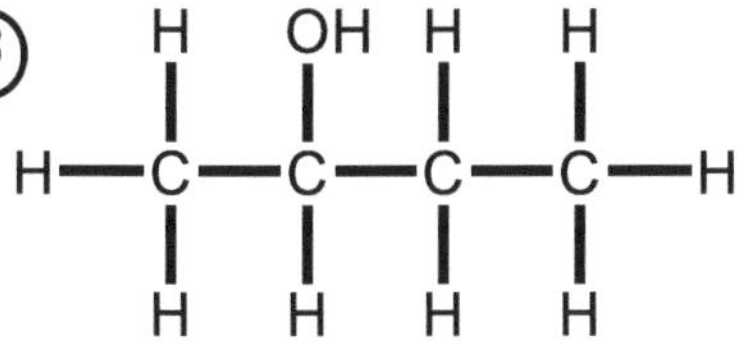

H—C—C—C—C—H

$CH_3CH(OH)CH_2CH_3$

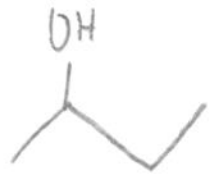

(C)

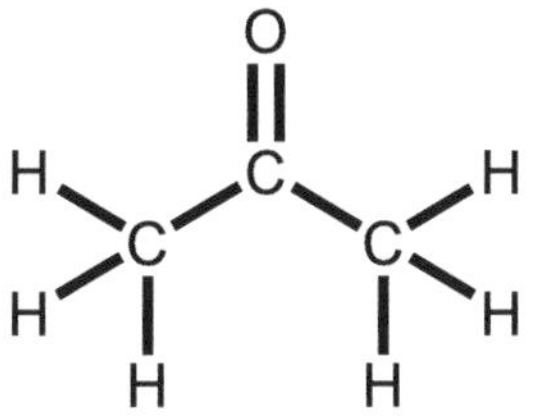

$CH_3C(O)CH_3$

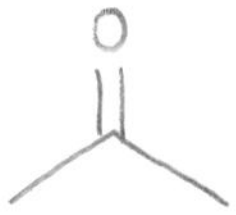

Notes

Since orbitals point in different directions, it should not be surprising that bonds point in various directions, and that molecules are three-dimensional. Chemists use a simple shorthand, called the "dash-wedge notation" in order to attempt to indicate a molecules 3D shape on 2D paper. It's not too complicated ...

A "regular" line indicates a bond that lies
(A) in the plane

A "wedge" indicates a bond that is
(B) closer to viewer

far   clok

A "dashed wedge" indicates a bond that is
(C) further from viewer

closer   far

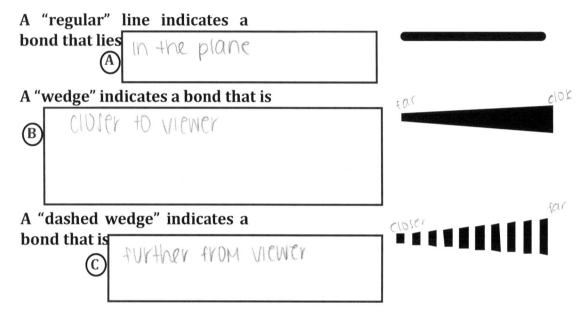

Notes

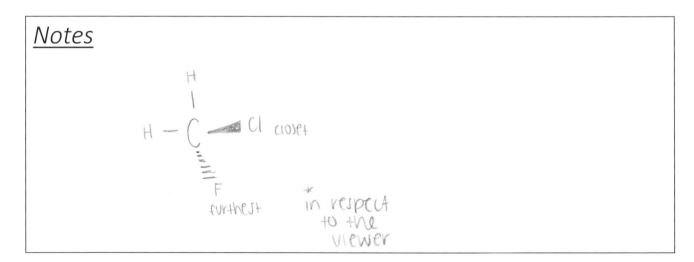

H
|
H — C ◄ Cl closet
⋮
F
furthest   in respect
to the
viewer

ionic bonds: "Complete" transfer of electrons to give two ions

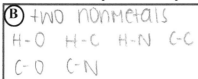

cation   anion

covalent bonds: Equal or Unequal sharing of electrons without "complete" transfer

(B) two nonmetals
H-O   H-C   H-N   C-C
C-O   C-N

A bond can be represented by two dots or by a line.

A line represents two electrons!

The extent to which the electron is transferred depends upon how strongly each atom attracts the electrons within the bond. This attractive force is called the ELECTRONEGATIVITY of the atoms.

Electronegativity (EN): pull of electrons by an atom in a bond
    increases ↑→ towards F in the periodic table

Notes

The difference in electronegativity (EN) of two bonded atoms will tell you to what extent the electrons in the bond are transferred from one atom to the other.

$$H—H$$
$$EN = 2.1 \ \ 2.1$$

$$Cl—Cl$$
$$EN = 3.0 \ \ 3.0$$

$\Delta EN = 0$ equal sharing of electrons
= _nonpolar_.

$$\overset{\delta^+}{H}—\overset{\delta^-}{Cl}$$
$$EN = 2.1 \ \ 3.0$$

$\Delta EN = 0.9$ unequal sharing of electrons
= _polar_.

$$Na^+Cl^-$$
$$EN = 0.9 \ \ 3.0$$

$\Delta EN = 2.1$ transfer of electrons
= _ionic_.

general rule: $\Delta EN <$ _1.9_ = "covalent"
$>$ _1.9_ = "ionic"

Δ = uppercase "delta". In science and math, delta often represents a change or difference.

Notes   C N O F   all
       P S Cl   polar
          Br   w/ C
           I

δ^+, δ^-

These are lowercase "delta" symbols. In science and math, delta often represents a change or a difference.

(A) *partial charges*

these lowercase Greek symbols ('delta') tell us that the atom above which they are written bear a partial positive or negative charge.

$$\overset{\delta^+}{H}-\overset{\delta^-}{F}$$

+⟶

The dipole moment is represented by 'mu', the greek 'm'.

(B) An arrow can also be used to represent the pull of electrons in the direction of the arrow. To emphasize the direction of electron movement, a 'plus' sign is drawn at the other side of the arrow. These arrows show us the

dipole moment

of the molecule.

+⟶
H—F

Notes

Formal charge =_valence - bonds - non bonded lone e-_

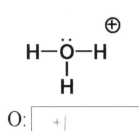

H—Ö—H ⊕
   |
   H

O: [+1]

H ⊕
|
H—C
|
H

C: [+1]

H ⊖
|
H—C—Ö:
|
H

C: [0]
O: [-1]

:N≡N—N̈: ⊖
 1   2   3

N#1: [0]
N#2: [+1]
N#3: [-2]

N̈=N=N̈ ⊖
1   2   3

N#1: [-1]
N#2: [+1]
N#3: [-1]

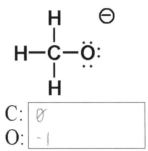

:C≡O: carbon
        monoxide

C: [-1]
O: [+1]

Notes

There are three types of intermolecular forces of focus in organic chemistry:

stronger

i. *Hydrogen Bonding* $\overset{\delta^-}{O}-\overset{\delta^+}{H}$ $\overset{\delta^-}{N}-\overset{\delta^+}{H}$

ii. *Dipole-Dipole interactions*
    any two polar molecules

iii. *van der Waals interactions* (London dispersion forces).
     non polar molecules

weaker

Notes

In a solid or liquid, it is the intermolecular forces that hold molecules close together:

In a molecular solid, energy is needed to break the molecules apart so they may flow past one another to form a liquid (melting).

In a molecular liquid, energy is needed to give the molecules enough kinetic energy to allow them to break away from the liquid surface and enter the gas phase (boiling).

It takes more energy to disrupt stronger intermolecular forces, so:

Melting point and boiling point both _____increase_____ as the

strength of intermolecular forces_____increase_____.

Notes   Rank

H bond   d-d   van der waals   d-d
                                           H bond

2   3   4   1

14

Nucleophile: "nucleus loving"; attracted to positive charges

example:
 -anion ($Nu^{\ominus} \rightarrow H^+$)
 -lone pair ($Nu: \rightarrow H^+$)
 -loosely-held bonding pair $\left(:C \overset{\sigma}{\underset{\pi}{=}} C: \right)$

Electrophile: "electron loving"; attracted to negative charges

example:
   - cation (E^+)
   - positive pole of polar bond
   - empty orbital on atom w/ less than an octet

Notes   sp²

Hydrocarbons

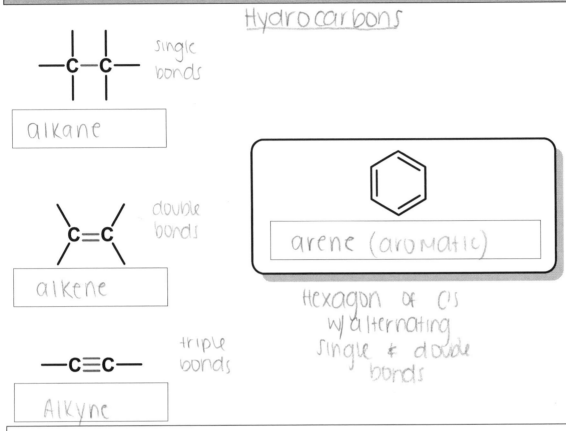

single bonds

alkane

double bonds

alkene

triple bonds

Alkyne

arene (aromatic)

Hexagon of C's
w/ alternating
single & double
bonds

Notes

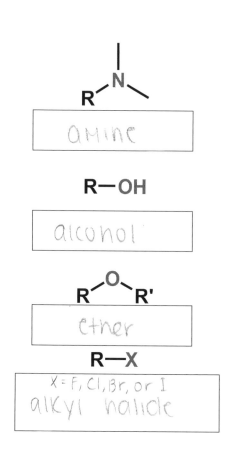

amine

R—OH

alcohol

ether

R—X

X = F, Cl, Br, or I
alkyl halide

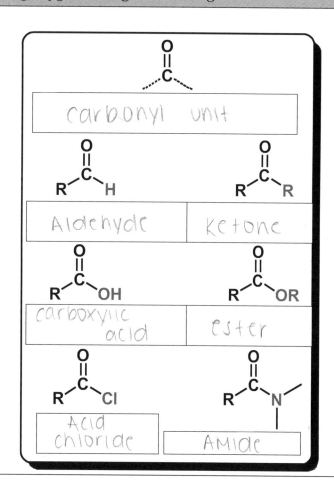

carbonyl unit

Aldehyde | Ketone

carboxylic acid | ester

Acid chloride | Amide

Notes

17

Circle and label each non-alkane functional group in the structure of Taxol, a chemotherapeutic drug:

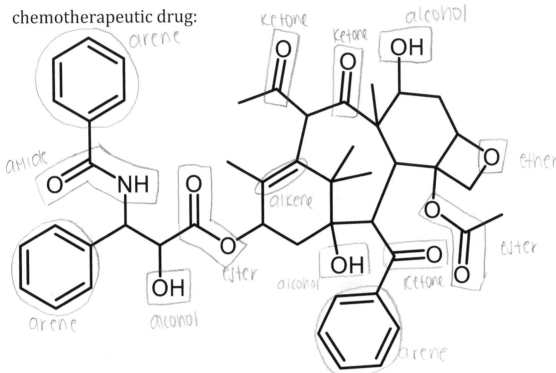

Notes

Circle and label each non-alkane functional group in the structure of Taxol, a chemotherapeutic drug:

Solution:

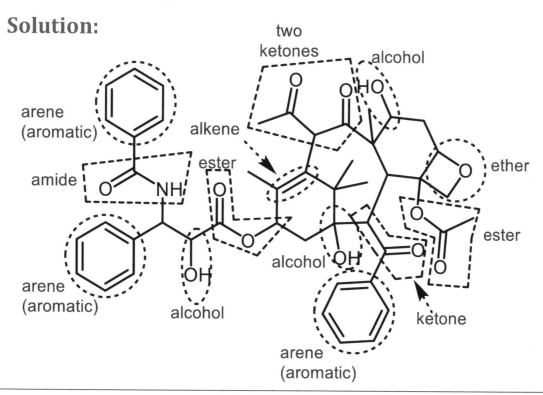

Notes

Since bonds consist of electrons between nuclei, the movement of electrons leads to changes in bonding; in other words **Chemical Reactions** are described by showing how the electrons rearrange upon going from reactants to products. In order to show the movement of electrons, we need a notation that is clear.

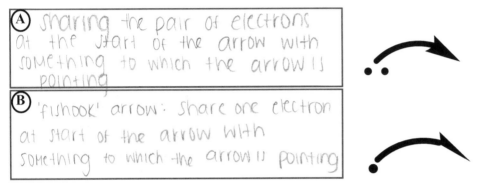

(A) Sharing the pair of electrons at the start of the arrow with something to which the arrow is pointing

(B) 'fishook' arrow: share one electron at start of the arrow with something to which the arrow is pointing

Electrons move FROM a good electron source (a lone pair or an anion, or the negative end of a polar bond ...) TO a good electron acceptor or "sink" (the positive end of a polar bond, an empty orbital, a cation ...).

Electrons move FROM a good electron source (a lone pair or an anion, or the negative end of a polar bond ...) TO a good electron acceptor or "sink" (the positive end of a polar bond, an empty orbital, a cation ...).

Notes

$H^{\oplus}$:ÖH$^{\ominus}$ → H-Ö-H

acid   base

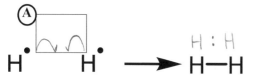

Two hydrogen atoms react to form H_2; each gives one electron, so use fishhook arrows

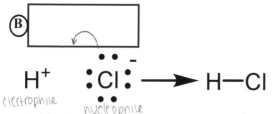

electrophile   nucleophile

A chloride anion and a proton react to form HCl; chloride donates a pair of electrons, so use a standard arrow.

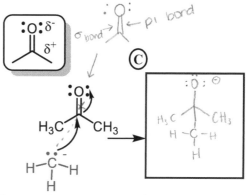

Here we show a more complicated 'cascade' of two arrows. The methyl anion electron pair (a good electron source) attacks the positive end of the polar C=O bond. That carbon already has 8 electrons, so 2 electrons have to move away from carbon, towards the more electronegative O atom that has a pull for electrons.

Notes

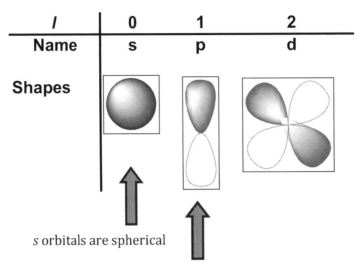

l	0	1	2
Name	**s**	**p**	**d**

Shapes

s orbitals are spherical

p orbitals are hourglass-shaped
There are three *p* orbitals in each shell;
One on each of the axes (x, y, and z)

Notes Carbons only use s & p orbitals

Two Orbitals can combine ...

... by adding ...

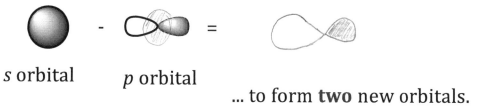

s orbital   p orbital

... or by subtracting ...

s orbital   p orbital

... to form **two** new orbitals.

Adding or "hybridizing" one s orbital with one p orbital gives two
   sp   hybrid orbitals.

Notes

Drawing both sp hybrid orbitals on the same atom:

This is an ___sp hybridized___ carbon atom.

The *sp* orbitals are pointed directionally ___180°___

from one another, resulting in a ___linear___ geometry.

Since carbon has three *p* orbitals and we only used one to make the hybrids, two *p* orbital are still left unhybridized on carbon:

Notes C: S + 3p
           -(-(
      2 p left on
         carbon

s orbital

three *sp*² **hybrid orbitals**.

Drawing all three sp² hybrid orbitals on the same atom:

This is an **sp² hybridized** carbon atom. The *sp²* orbitals are in a plane pointed directionally

_____120°_____

from one another, towards the corners of an equilateral triangle in a

1 p leftover

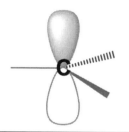

_____triganol planar_____ geometry.

Since carbon has three *p* orbitals and we only used two to make the hybrids, a p orbital is still left unhybridized on carbon.

Notes

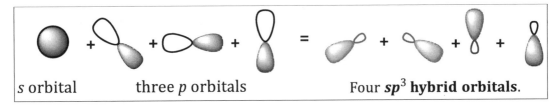

s orbital   three *p* orbitals   Four *sp*³ **hybrid orbitals**.

Drawing all four sp³ hybrid orbitals on the same atom:

This is an *sp*³ hybridized carbon atom. The sp³ orbitals are pointed directionally ___109.5°___

from one another, in a

___tetrahedral___ geometry.

Since carbon has three p orbitals and we used all three to make the hybrids, all of the valence orbitals are now *sp*³ orbitals, and consequently these are the only ones used in bonding.

Notes

A sigma (σ) bond is one in which the electrons making the bond are between the two nuclei joined by the bond:

electrons sit on the
internuclear axis

H :H

A pi (π) bond is one in which the electrons lie above and below the line between the two nuclei which are joined by the bond:

a total of 2 electrons
sit in the approximate
regions to which the
arrow points

In the vast majority of examples in introductory organic, the **hybrid orbitals** will form sigma bonds or will be filled by a lone pair of electrons, and any pi bonds will be made by p orbitals not hybridized into sp, sp^2, or sp^3 orbitals...

Notes

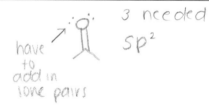

H   H
need 4
sp^3

need 3
sp^2

have
to
add in
lone pairs

3 needed
sp^2

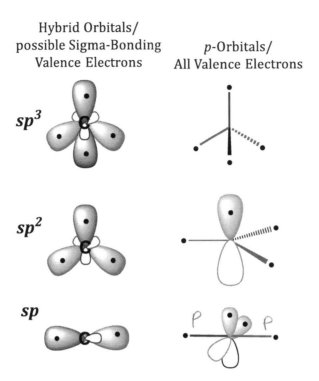

Hybrid Orbitals/
possible Sigma-Bonding
Valence Electrons

p-Orbitals/
All Valence Electrons

sp³

sp²

sp

<u>Notes</u>

We can bind two sp^3 hybridized carbons together
and make sigma bonds to hydrogen atoms with
the remaining sp^3 orbitals

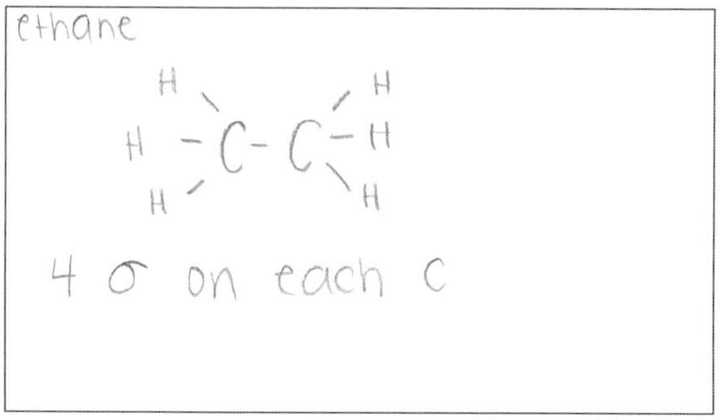

ethane

H   H
 \   /
H - C - C - H
  /   \
 H   H

4 σ on each C

This is ETHANE. There are
no more valence orbitals, so
we can make no more bonds.

Notes

creates double
bond w two
p orbitals

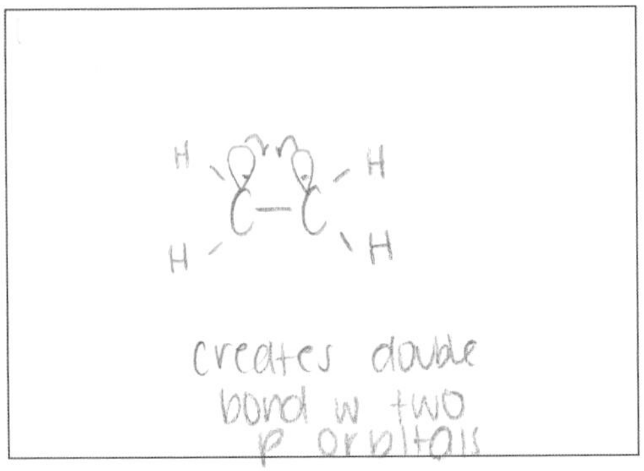

3 σ or lone pairs

In Ethylene, the sp^2 hybrid orbitals form sigma bonds with C and H.

We have a pi orbital left over on each carbon, each with one electron. These two orbitals overlap to form a pi bond, so ethylene's line-bond structure is:

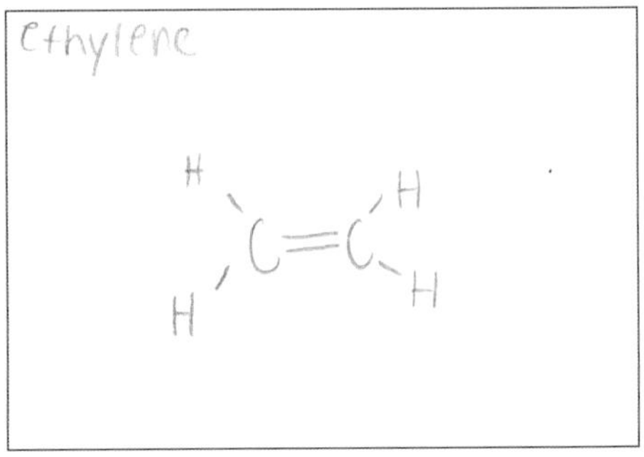

ethylene

Notes

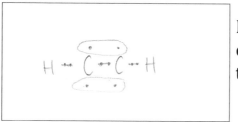

two σ bonds

In acetylene, the *sp*-hybrid orbitals are again used to make the sigma bonds.

Each of the two *sp*-hybridized carbon atoms has two *p* orbitals left unhybridized, so there will be two pi bonds formed between the carbon atoms, yielding acetylene's line-bond structure:

alkyne

$$H - C \equiv C - H$$

Notes

Electronegativity is how strongly an atom holds its electrons in a bond. How strongly electrons are held depends on the orbital that holds the electrons:

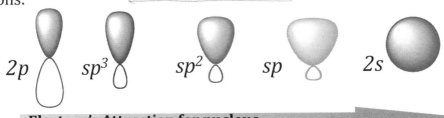

further from nucleus

$2p$ sp^3 sp^2 sp $2s$

Electron's Attraction for nucleus

An orbital that has more (**A**) *s- character*
has a greater pull on electrons.

So, the electronegativity trend is:

(**B**) *sp hybridized > sp² hybridized > sp³- hybridized*

An *sp* hybridized C atom has about the **same electronegativity** as an sp^3-hybridized N atom

Notes

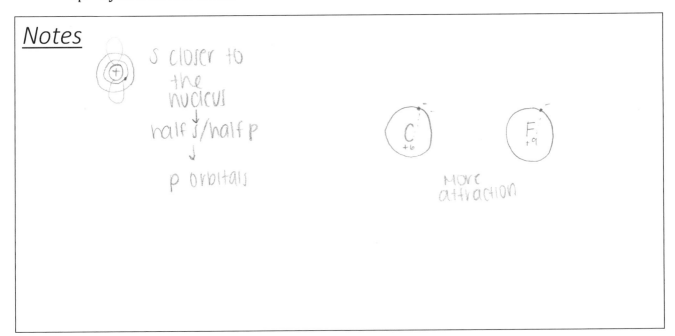

s closer to the nucleus
half s/half p
↓
p orbitals

C +6

F +9

More attraction

32

In a resonance structure the atomic positions remain the same, but electrons move around (lone pairs and <u>multiple</u> bond positions change).

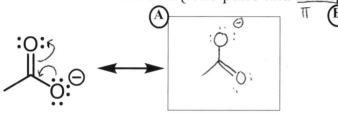

(A)   π   (B)

neither resonance form alone accurately describes the anion; the "real" structure is a combination of the two, as shown at right

Resonance Hybrid
(dashed line = partial bond)

<u>Why do we care?</u> Resonance structures can help us understand reactivity. If a molecule can be drawn in numerous resonance forms, it has some added stability known as: if there is resonance it is more stable than no resonance
(resonance stabilization)
This extra stability is due to: delocalization (spread over more volume or atoms)

Notes — no double bond cannot perform resonance

Never points to negative charge

less stable   More stable

⊖ M small volume =bad

spread out ⊖ big volume = good

Electrons move FROM a good electron source (a lone pair or an anion, or the negative end of a polar bond ...) TO a good electron acceptor or "sink" (the positive end of a polar bond, an empty orbital, a cation ...).

RESONANCE
Hybrid

all correct
representation
of the
Molecule

⟷   Note the special resonance arrow

⇌   Not to be confused with the
equilibrium arrow!
RESONANCE IN NOT AN EQUILIBRIUM!

Notes

We are not yet attempting to predict when or explain why these steps take place, but you should be able to 1. recognize which step is happening given reactants/reagents; 2. provide the arrows necessary for a transformation or 3. provide product(s) given reagent(s) and arrow(s).

two things work tg

coordination

different
hetero lysis
cutting

1. $B^{\ominus}$ ⤳ E^+ —— **coordination** ——→
←—— **heterolysis** ——
$B—E$

2. *arrow to atom*
$\overset{R}{\underset{\oplus}{C—C}}$ —— **carbocation rearrangement** ——→ $\overset{R}{\underset{\oplus}{C—C}}$

carbon positive rearranging

3. E^+ —— **electrophilic addition** ——→
←—— **electrophilic elimination** ——
$\overset{\oplus}{\diagdown}$ E
arrow to space

*E^+ addition
adding a +
breaking a π bond*

*E^+ elimination
makes π bond
thing comes off has ⊕*

Notes

NAME	Substitution	addition	elimination
- coordination	- SN2 (s-substitution)	break π	makes π bond
- heterolysis	σ for dif σ	-E^+ addition	-E^+ elimination
- carbocation rearrangement		+nucle adds	-E_2 (E= elimination)
			-nucleo elimination

35

only rxn step w/ 3 arrows

(4.)

E2 reaction

$+ BH + LG^{\ominus}$

one breaks @ same time
one made

(5.)

$Nu^{\ominus}$ $R—LG$ $\xrightarrow{\text{S}_\text{N}\text{2 reaction}}$ $R—Nu + LG^{\ominus}$

(6.)

Nu

**nucleophilic
addition**

**nucleophilic
elimination**

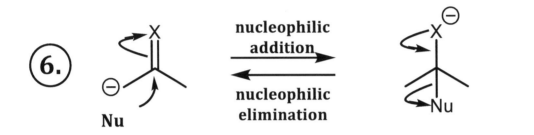

Notes

Here are some examples of coordination and heterolysis. Protonation is a common example of coordination and deprotonation is a common example of heterolysis.

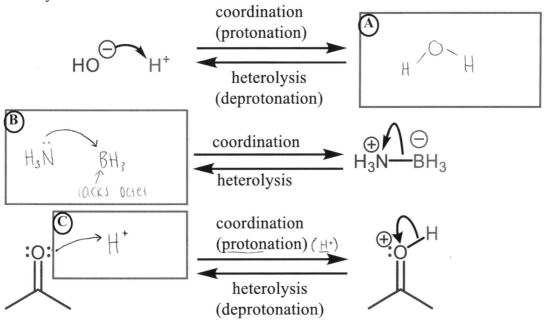

coordination
(protonation)

heterolysis
(deprotonation)

(A)

coordination

heterolysis

coordination
(protonation) (H^+)

heterolysis
(deprotonation)

(B)

$H_3\ddot{N}$ BH_3

lacks octet

(C)

:O: H^+

<u>Notes</u>

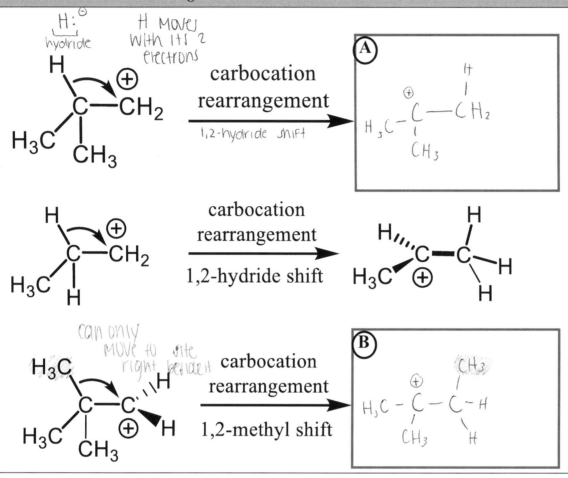

Notes

38

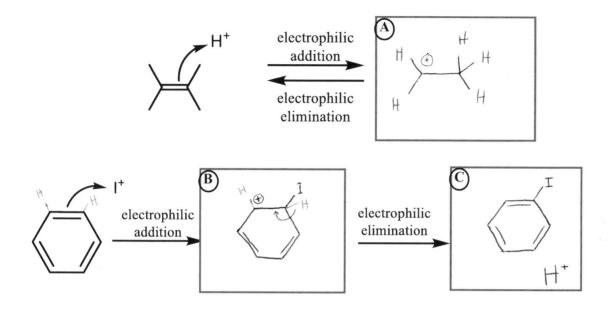

Notes

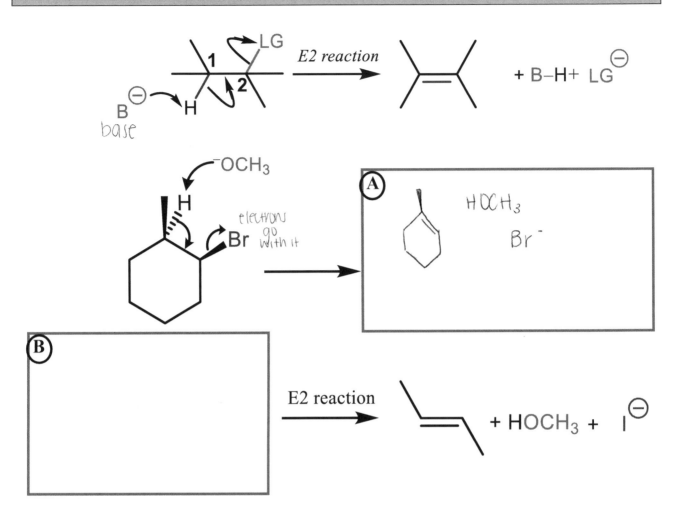

E2 reaction

+ B–H+ LG$^{\ominus}$

$^{-}$OCH$_3$

electrons
go
with it

A   HOCH$_3$

Br^{-}

B

E2 reaction

+ HOCH$_3$ + I$^{\ominus}$

base

Br

Notes

S$_N$2 reaction

S$_N$2 reaction

A

Br⁻

B

S$_N$2 reaction

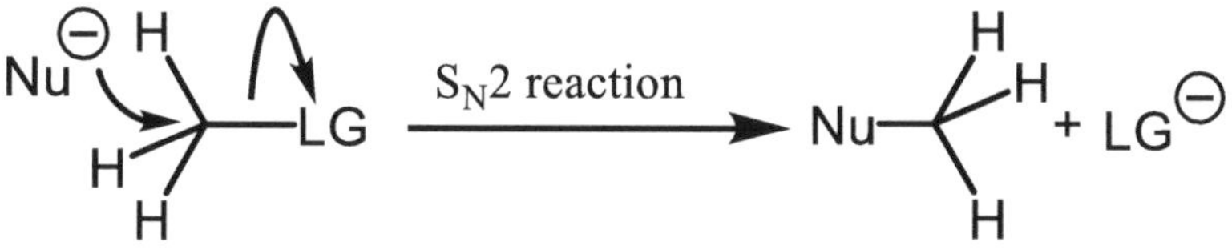

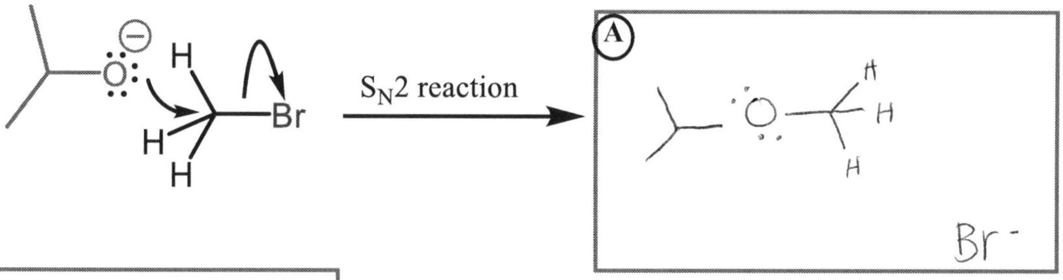

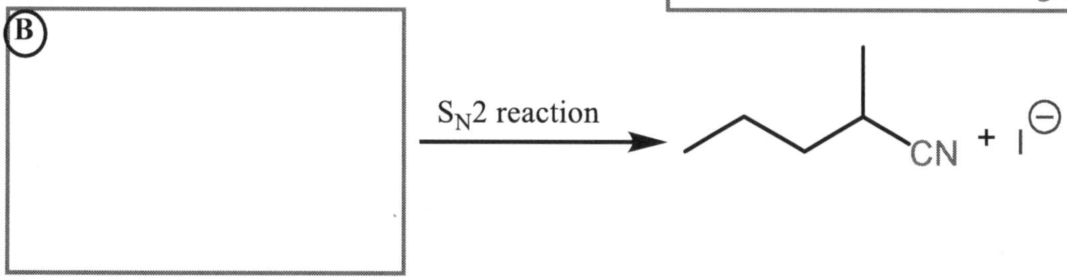

Notes

Lecture Topic I.8: Elementary Steps of Reaction Mechanisms
Nucleophilic Addition and Elimination

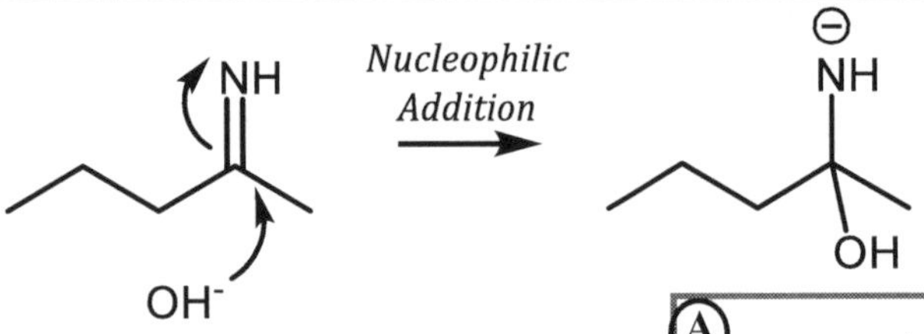

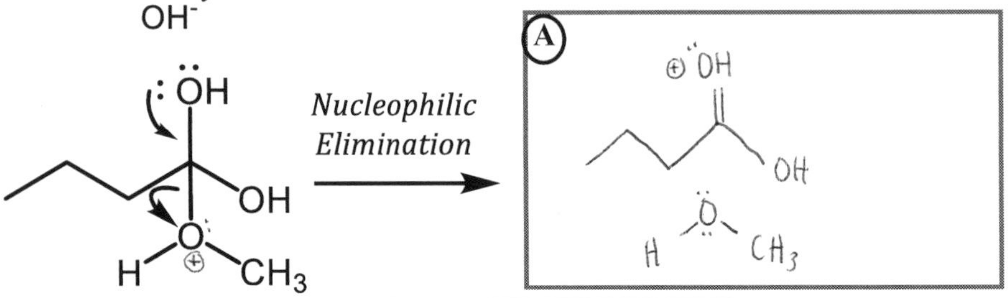

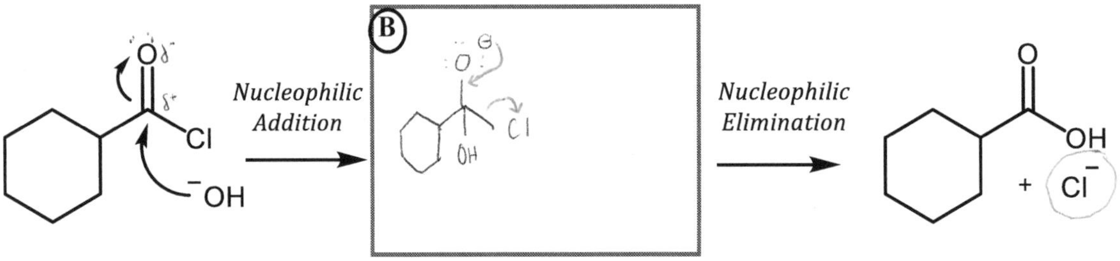

Nucleophilic Addition

Nucleophilic Elimination

(A)

(B)

Nucleophilic Addition

Nucleophilic Elimination

Notes

In General Chemistry we learned about acids and bases, pH, pK_a, etc. We will briefly review some of these ideas. There are various ways to think about acid-base reactions.

Examples

Arrhenius Definition
acid: dissociates to give H^+
base: dissociates to give OH^-

acid: HNO_3, HCl
base: $NaOH$

Brønsted-Lowry Definition
acid: proton donor (give H^+)
base: proton acceptor (takes H^+)

acid: HNO_3, HCl, HI
base: HO^-
base: NH_3, $^-CH_3$

Lewis Definition
acid: electron pair acceptor
base: electron pair donor

acid: BH_3, $^{\oplus}CH_3$, H^+
base: $:NH_3$, $H_2\ddot{O}:$

*recall that in water H^+ forms the hydronium ion, H_3O^+

Notes

Brønsted-lowry Base
$$HA + \ddot{B} \longrightarrow \overset{+}{B}H + A^-$$

Lewis acid base
$$H_3B + H_2O \longrightarrow H - \overset{H}{\underset{H}{\overset{|}{B}}} \overset{\ominus}{-} \overset{H}{\underset{\oplus}{\overset{|}{O}}} - H$$

One important skill to develop in organic chemistry is to be able to determine the predominant protonation state of a species in a solution of a certain pH. As a general rule of thumb, a site will keep its proton until the pH of the solution is higher than the pK_a for that site.

Consider phosphoric acid (H_3PO_4), which has pK_{a1} = 2.2, pK_{a2} = 7.2, pK_{a3} = 12.3.

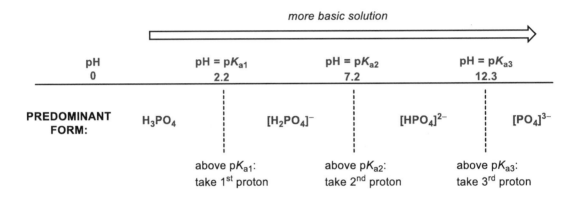

Notes

$H\text{-}A \rightleftharpoons H^+ + A^-$

$K_a = \dfrac{[H^+][A^-]}{[HA]}$

$pK_a = -\log[K_a]$

$K_a \uparrow \quad pK_a \downarrow$
acidity $\uparrow$

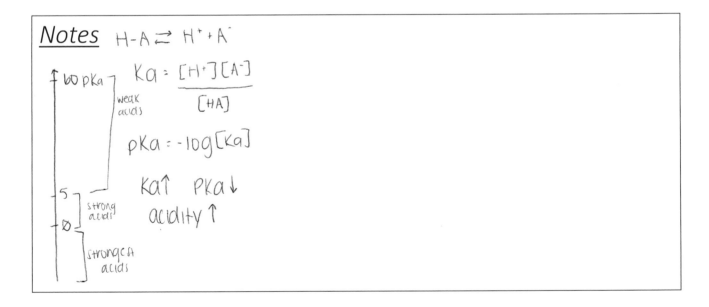

Example. Citric acid has three common protonation states. What protonation state will predominate at pH = a) 2, b) 3, c) 5, d) 6, and e) 7?

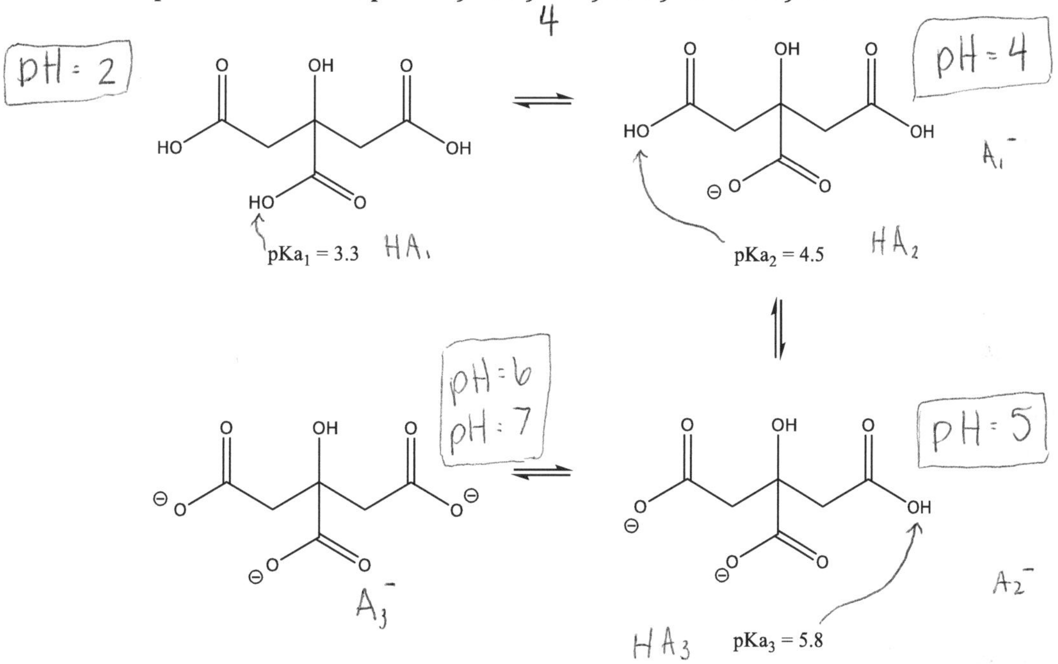

4

pH = 2

pH = 4

$pKa_1 = 3.3$ HA₁

$pKa_2 = 4.5$ HA₂

A_1^-

pH = 6
pH = 7

pH = 5

A_3^-

HA₃ $pKa_3 = 5.8$

A_2^-

Notes

$$HA + H_2O \rightleftharpoons A^- + H_3O^+$$

acid   conjugate
                                base

Any factors that favor dissociation of HA into H^+ (to form H_3O^+ in water) and A^- will enhance acidity.

Most important factor influencing dissociation:

*1. Stability of conjugate Base

Notes The More stable the conjugate base,
     the More acidic the compound

The More acidic the acid,
    the weaker the base
    -less basic -More stable

Within a group (column), the size of the anion has a strong effect on acidity, because:

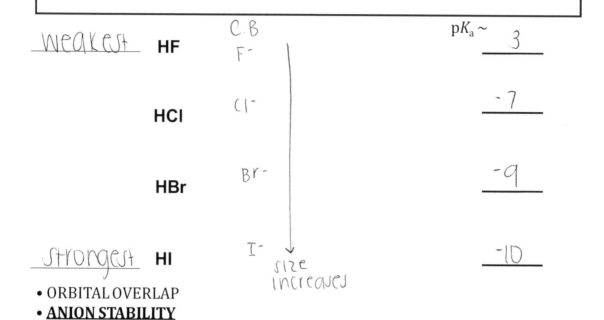

weakest **HF**   C.B pK_a ~   3
                      F⁻

          HCl   Cl⁻   -7

          HBr   Br⁻   -9

strongest **HI**   I⁻   -10
                      size
                      increases

- ORBITAL OVERLAP
- **ANION STABILITY**

<u>Notes</u>   5 factors affect stability of conjugate base

  - electronegativity   SERI

  - size

  - hybridization

  - resonance

  - inductive effect

  ✳ in a (group)
              column   size is predominant ✳

The electronegativity plays a strong role because: $\longrightarrow$ electronegativity increases

* Electronegativity is a measure of attraction for electrons

  $\rightarrow$ Higher EN, the more stable conjugate base b/c the more EN atom can attract electrons better

C.B.	$(^-CH_3)$	$(^-NH_2)$	(HO^-)	(F^-)
	CH_4	NH_3	H_2O	HF

weakest acid   strongest acid

$pK_a \sim$ 50   38   14   3

* $^-CH_3$ most basic

Notes

If the atom to be deprotonated is the same and only hybridization changes, we need to know that the hybridization influences electronegativity:

pKa   51   44   25

acidity $sp > sp_2 > sp_3$

Acetylide anion

Note: the electronegativity of an *sp*-hybridized C is similar to that of an sp^3-hybridized N

Notes   same atoms
            then
        - hybridization
        - resonance
        - inductive effect

If the anion produced by deprotonation has more than one (good) resonance form, then:

the anion is more stable than the comparable anion with no resonance (resonance = delocalized e-)

HF
$pK_a = 3.1$

F- F > O ⇒ most stable, strongest acid

CH₃CO₂H
$pK_a = 4.7$

$H_3 C-C \overset{O}{\underset{\overset{..}{O}:}{\|}} \ominus$ ⟷ $H_3C-C \overset{O^-}{\underset{O}{|}}$

resonance ↑
stability ↑

CH₃OH
$pK_a = 15.5$

$CH_3 - \overset{..}{\underset{..}{O}}: ^-$

no resonance
weakest acid
least stable

Notes

Inductive effects can make a species more OR less acidic. If an atom to be deprotonated has a partial positive charge INDUCED on it by nearby atoms, it is easier to deprotonate because: there is a stabilizing attractive force between anionic atom and the positive charge

MOST polar bond greater $\delta +$
MOre stabilizing

| pKa | 4.8 | 3.2 | 2.9 | 2.8 | 2.7 |

This series illustrates: F > Cl > Br > I
    a stronger polar bond (greater $\delta +$) = MOre stabilizing

| pKa | Br 3.0 | 4.0 | Br 4.6 |

This series illustrates:
    a polar bond closer to deprotonated site = MOre stabilizing

Notes

sterics:
the lone pair on the anionic ion will repel
nearby bonding pairs
so, the more/bigger (branches) at site adjacent to deprotonated
atom leads to lower and weaker conjugate acid

$pK_a \sim$ ____16____   ____17____   ____18____

____16.1____

as bulkiness ↑
the acidity ↓

Notes

Which is the strongest acid:

a) SiH_4 b) PH_3 c) SH_2 d) HCl — MOST electronegative, MOST stable

$H - \overset{H}{\underset{H}{Si}} - H$ $H - \overset{..}{\underset{H}{P}} - H$ $H - \overset{..}{\underset{..}{S}} \diagdown H$ $H - \overset{..}{\underset{..}{Cl}} :^{\ominus}$

Which is the strongest base:

a) H_3C^- b) H_2N^- c) HO^- d) F^- — MOST electronegative MOST acidic

CH_4 NH_3 H_2O HF

Which has the lowest pK_a: lowest pka = highest acid

CH_4 $H_3C - CH_3$ $H_2C = CH_2$ $HC \equiv CH$

sp^3 sp^3 sp^2 sp

(a)   (b)   (c)   (d) hybridization

Notes

Which proton shown in each molecule is most acidic?

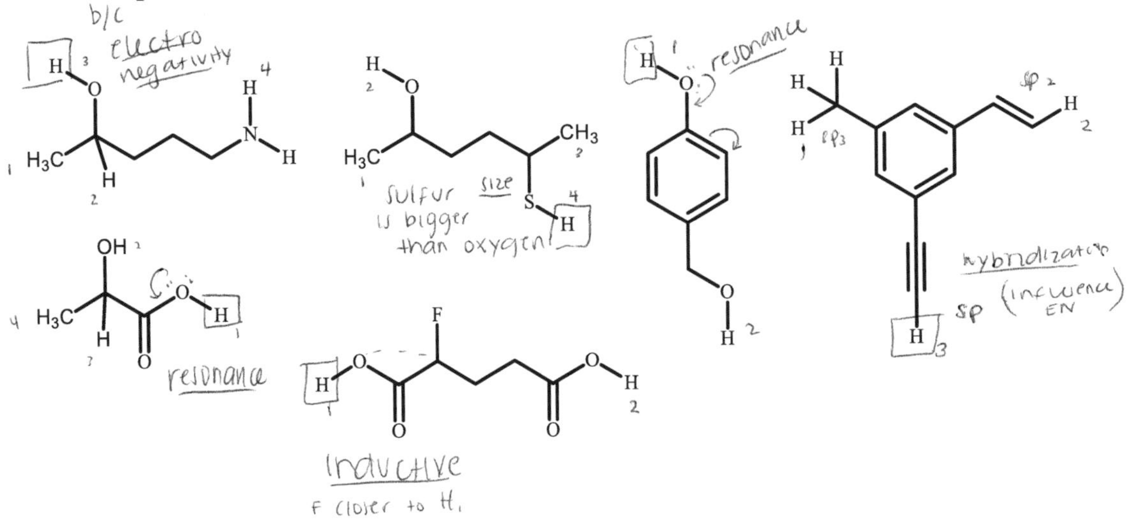

Molecule annotations:

b/c electro negativity

sulfur size is bigger than oxygen!

resonance

resonance

inductive — F closer to H₁

hybridization — sp (influence) EN

sp₂

lp₃

Notes

Ⓐ **Observation**

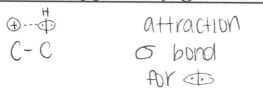

More substituted = more stable

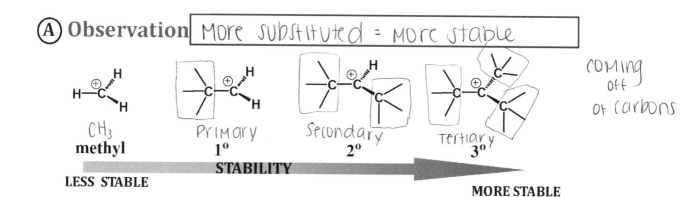

coming off of carbons

CH_3
methyl

Primary
1°

Secondary
2°

Tertiary
3°

STABILITY

LESS STABLE   **MORE STABLE**

Ⓑ **Explanation: Hyperconjugation**

attraction
σ bond
for

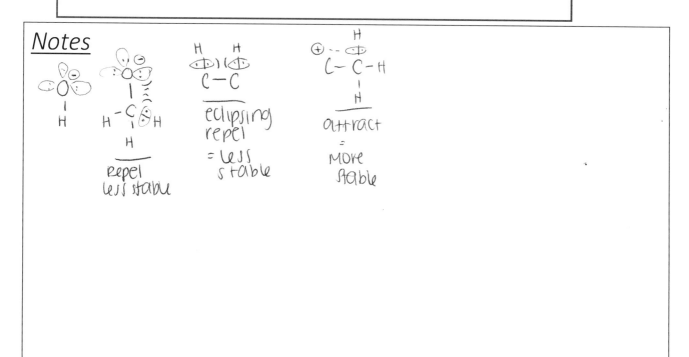

Notes

repel
less stable

eclipsing
repel
= less
stable

attract
=
More
stable

Lecture Topic I.11: Stability of Carbocations and Alkenes
Resonance Stabilizes Carbocations

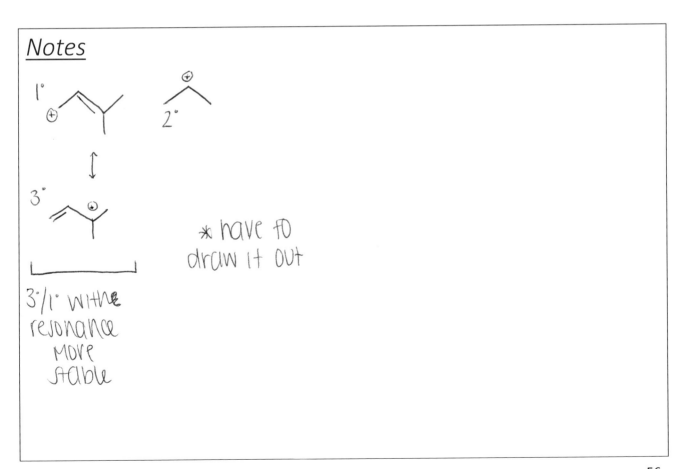

STABILITY

LESS STABLE   **MORE STABLE**

Notes

1°

2°

3°

3°/1° with resonance more stable

* have to draw it out

We observe the following trend in alkene stability:

1. More substituted = More stable

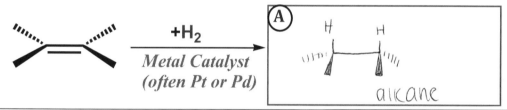

eclipsing

cis-   trans-

STABILITY

LESS STABLE   MORE STABLE

These stabilities are determined by doing a **hydrogenation** of the alkene and measuring the heat given off by the process. Hydrogenation (**addition of two H atoms to the pi bond**) is accomplished by reacting with $H_2(g)$ and a Pd or Pt catalyst:

+H₂

Metal Catalyst (often Pt or Pd)

(A)   H   H

alkane

Notes

$C=C$

EN

$sp^2 > sp^3$

57

Heat of Hydrogenation tells us about: (A) stability

A more stable alkene has a (B) lower amount of heat release

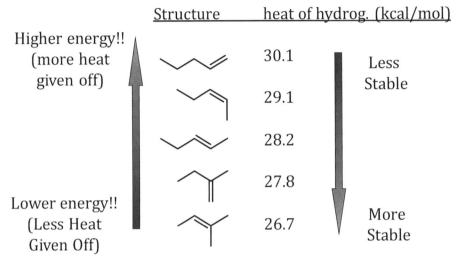

	Structure	heat of hydrog. (kcal/mol)	
Higher energy!! (more heat given off)		30.1	Less Stable
		29.1	
		28.2	
		27.8	
Lower energy!! (Less Heat Given Off)		26.7	More Stable

Notes

—unstable

favorable & spontaneous

energy

- stable

Thermodynamically Favorable (Spontaneous):

go from less stable to more stable
(high energy)   (low energy)

Example: Assuming that each process is mechanistically accessible, use your knowledge of stability trends to predict whether formation of product would be thermodynamically favorable (spontaneous):

A) 2° → 3° ← More stable

B) More EN (OH⁻) + (amine N-H) → H_2O + (amine N⁻) More stable

C) H⁻ Smaller + (amine N-H) → H_2 + (amine N⁻) Bigger More stable

For anion
S
E
R
I

New rules for cation

Notes

Lecture Topic I.12: Predicting Reaction Spontaneity and Direction of Equilibria
Predicting Direction of Equilibria

Definition of Equilibrium: rate → = rate ←

Equations: $K_{eq} = \frac{[products]}{[reactants]}$ More products $K_{eq} > 1$

Nucleophilic addition example :

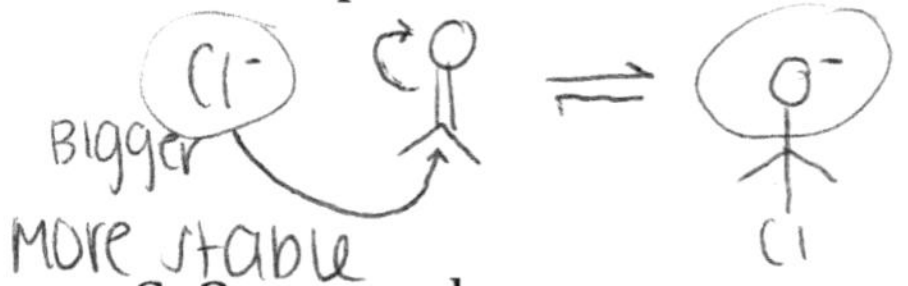
Cl⁻
Bigger
More stable
O⁻
Cl

$Cl^- > O^-$ not spontaneous

S_N2 example:

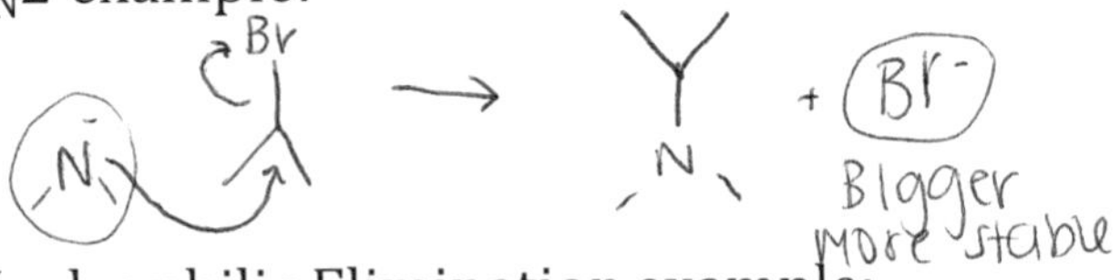
Br
N
Br⁻
Bigger
More stable

spontaneous

Nucleophilic Elimination example:

Notes

Stability	lower energy = more stable
Spontaneity:	products lower energy than reactants
Reaction Rate:	faster if Ea is lower

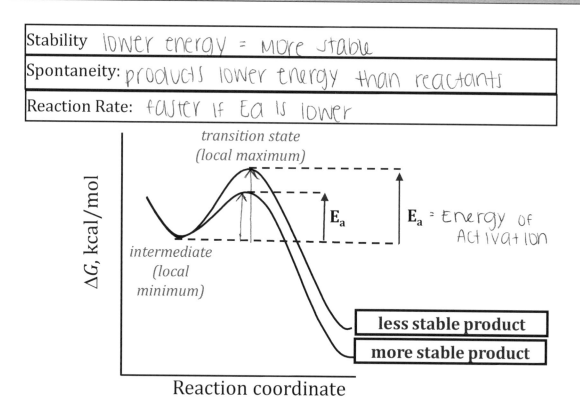

transition state
(local maximum)

ΔG, kcal/mol

E_a

E_a = Energy of Activation

intermediate
(local
minimum)

less stable product

more stable product

Reaction coordinate

Notes

61

CH_4	
CH_3CH_3	
$CH_3CH_2CH_3$	
$CH_3(CH_2)_2CH_3$	
$CH_3(CH_2)_3CH_3$	
$CH_3(CH_2)_4CH_3$	
$n\text{-}C_7H_{16}$	
$n\text{-}C_8H_{18}$	
$n\text{-}C_9H_{20}$	
$n\text{-}C_{10}H_{22}$	

Notes

Constitutional Isomers-

C_4H_{10}

linear alkanes
('*n*ormal' alkanes)

branched alkanes

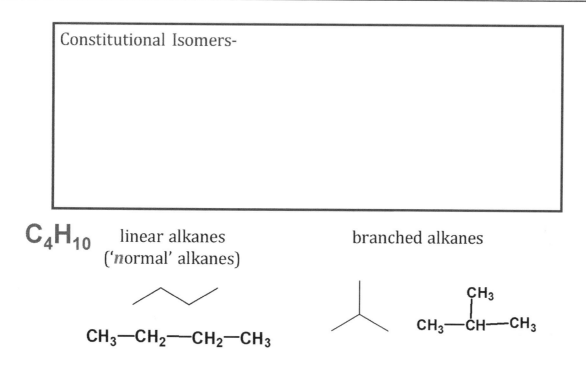

$CH_3—CH_2—CH_2—CH_3$

Lighter fluid is 5% *n*-butane and 95% isobutane

Notes

C_5H_{12}

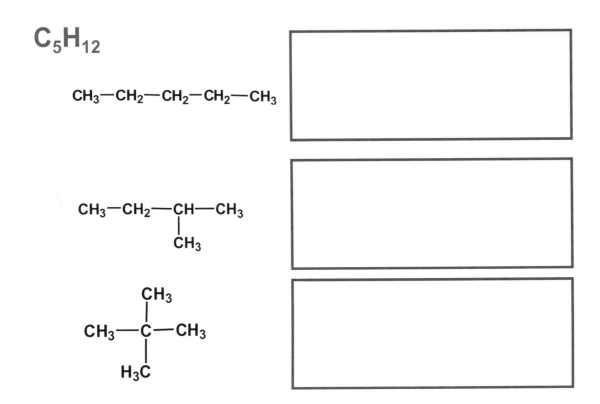

CH₃—CH₂—CH₂—CH₂—CH₃

CH₃—CH₂—CH—CH₃
　　　　　　|
　　　　　 CH₃

　　　 CH₃
　　　　|
CH₃—C—CH₃
　　　　|
　　 H₃C

Notes

Lecture Topic I.14: Nomenclature of Alkanes, Alkyl halides, Alcohols and Cycloalkanes
Stability of Linear vs. Branched Alkanes

Heats of combustion (ΔH_c) for burning C_8H_{18} isomers:

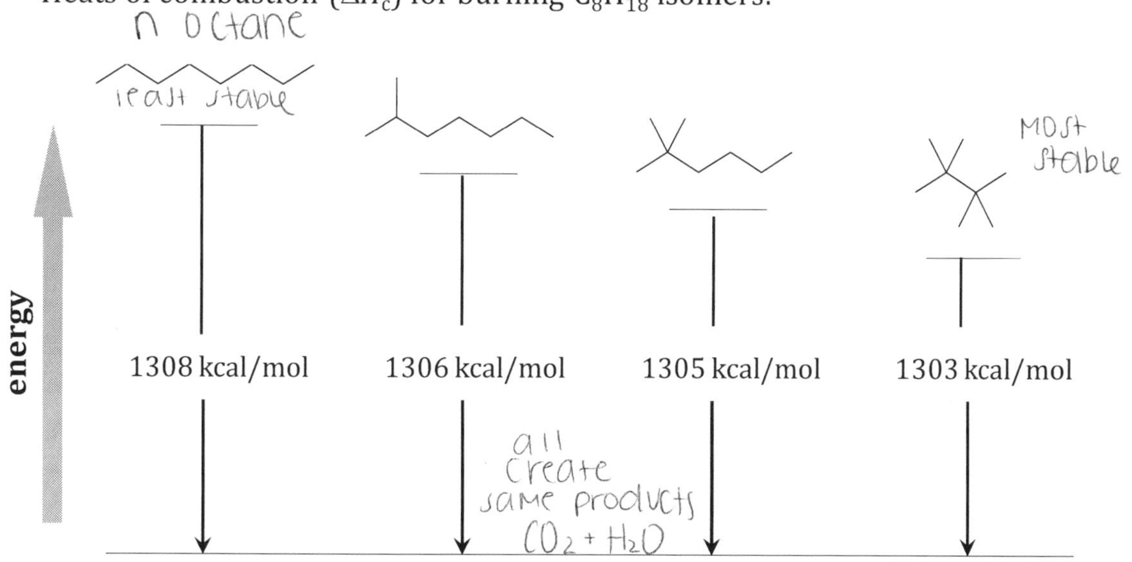
n octane
least stable
most stable
energy
1308 kcal/mol
1306 kcal/mol
1305 kcal/mol
1303 kcal/mol
all create same products
$CO_2 + H_2O$

The **more branching**, the **less heat released**, so
more branched = more stable alkane

Notes

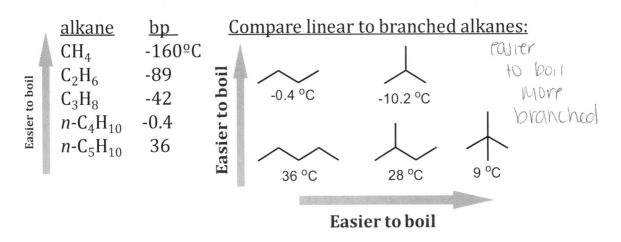

alkane	bp
CH_4	-160ºC
C_2H_6	-89
C_3H_8	-42
n-C_4H_{10}	-0.4
n-C_5H_{10}	36

Easier to boil

Compare linear to branched alkanes:

Easier to boil

-0.4 °C   -10.2 °C   *easier to boil more branched*

36 °C   28 °C   9 °C

Easier to boil

The **lighter** or **more branching**, the **less intermolecular force**, so

more branched = lower boiling point / lower melting pt.

Lighter = lower b.p.

Notes

66

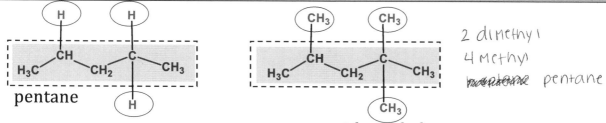

pentane

pentane with methyl groups
substituted for some of the hydrogens

2 dimethyl
4 methyl
~~pentane~~ pentane

Substituent: group coming off of longest
consecutive chain of atoms (parent chain)

Substituents that occur frequently in molecules of interest are given names to simplify naming a complex molecule.

Of course there are substituents other than methyl groups we can put on to a molecule ...

Notes

67

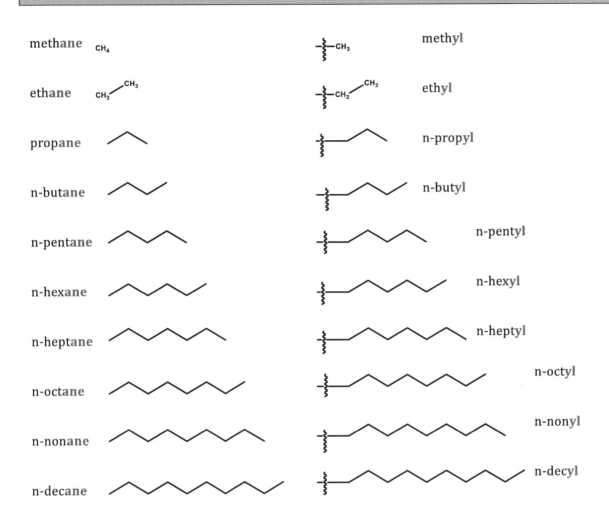

methane CH_4 methyl

ethane   ethyl

propane   n-propyl

n-butane   n-butyl

n-pentane   n-pentyl

n-hexane   n-hexyl

n-heptane   n-heptyl

n-octane   n-octyl

n-nonane   n-nonyl

n-decane   n-decyl

Notes

propane *n*-propyl "*n*-" indicates it is "normal", linear

propane isopropyl "*iso*-" indicates it has a 3-C, Y-shaped unit

n-butane *n*-butyl "*n*-" indicates it is "normal", linear

n-butane *sec*-butyl "*sec*-" indicates it is substituted at the secondary carbon

isobutane isobutyl "*iso*-" indicates it has a 3-C, Y-shaped unit

isobutane *tert*-butyl "*tert*-" indicates substitution at the tertiary carbon

Notes

r

69

Your step-by-step guide

1. Find parent chain

This is the 'parent chain'; the other stuff on the parent chain will be named as substituents. Be aware that there are many ways to draw the same molecule:

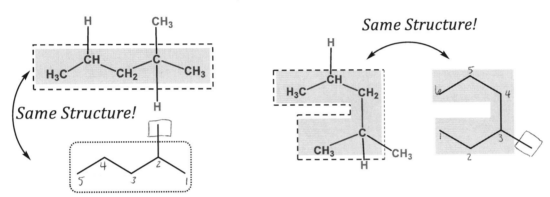

This is pentane, with one methyl ($-CH_3$) substituent ... regardless of how it is drawn!

Notes

2. Number the carbon atoms in the 'parent chain' in the way that gives the lowest number to the substituent closest to an end of the parent chain.

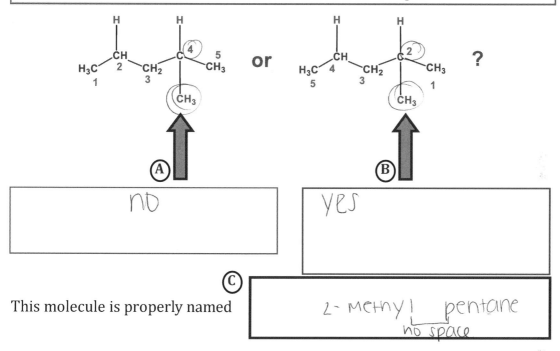

(A) no

(B) yes

(C) This molecule is properly named

2- Methyl   pentane
        no space

Notes

1. Find the longest chain

alkane   **possible parent chains:**

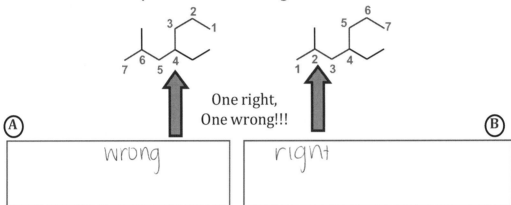

#C's: 6   6   6   7

2. Number the parent chain to give lowest number to substituent closest to end

possible numbering schemes:

One right,
One wrong!!!

Ⓐ

wrong

Ⓑ

right

Notes

3. With more than one type of substituent,

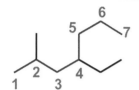

We could name it
2-methyl-4-ethylheptane
or
4-ethyl-2-methylheptane ✓ alphabetical

Since 'ethyl' is alphabetically before 'methyl', this molecule is
properly named

4-ethyl-2-Methylheptane

Now consider this closely related molecule, in which
the ethyl group is changed to a methyl group. The
numbering and parent chain are the same, but now
we have two methyl groups; we need to apply the
next rule ...

Notes

Prefixes Designate Multiple Substituents of one Type

4. If more than one of the same substituent are present on your parent chain, use di, tri, tetra, etc. prefixes to denote this (**these prefixes do not count when alphabetizing.** Neither do the *n*-, *sec*-, or *tert*- prefixes.

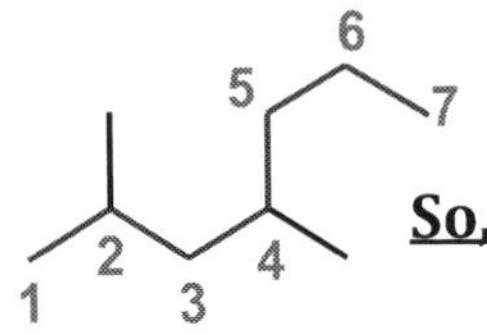

So, we call this

2,4-di Methylheptane

~~NOT~~
~~2-methyl-4-methylheptane~~
~~or~~
~~4-methyl-2-methylheptane~~

Incorrect names!

Notes

Alphabetically First Substituents Get the Lower Number in Case of a Tie

There are even more potential complications that could trip us up; consider:

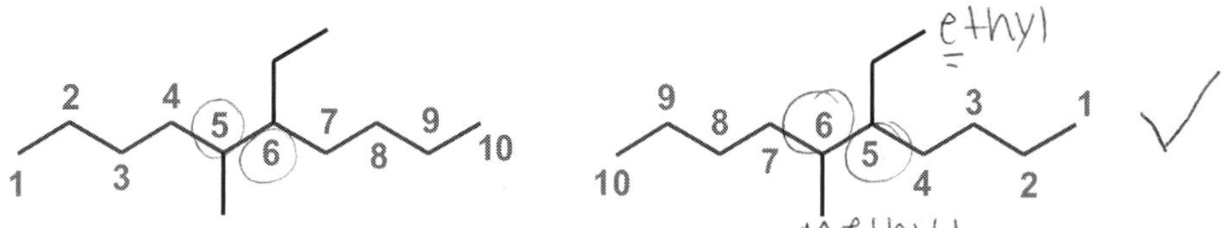

We've easily found the parent chain (decane), and we try to find the right numbering scheme; but either way we count, the first substituent is at the 5 position; which is right?
We need the next rule:

5. If numbering leads to the same "lowest number" substituent in both directions the correct numbering:
if tie low # goes to alphabetically first

In this case, ethyl is alphabetically before methyl, so ethyl is given the 5:
This molecule is properly named:

5-ethyl-6-methyl decane

Notes

The previous example showed you how to deal with substituent numbering issues; but what if you have trouble identifying the parent chain to begin with? Consider:

Two possible octane parent chains; which is right? We need another rule.

6. If you find two different possible parent chains of the same length,

choose one w/ most substituents

The one on the left has more substituents, so we use that parent chain.

This molecule is properly named:

2,4,6-trimethyl - 5 - propyloctane

tri

Notes

Your step-by-step guide to alkane nomenclature

6 rules

1. Find the longest chain. This is the 'parent chain'; the other stuff on the parent chain will be named as substituents. Be aware that there are many ways to draw the same molecule.
2. Number the carbon atoms in the 'parent chain' in the way that gives the lowest number to the substituent closest to an end of the parent chain.
3. With more than one type of substituent, name in alphabetical order.
4. If more than one of the same substituent are present on your parent chain, use di, tri, tetra, etc. prefixes to denote this (these prefixes do not count when alphabetizing, though; neither do the n-, sec-, or tert- prefixes)
5. If numbering leads to the same lowest number substituent in both directions the correct numbering gives the lowest number to the substituent that is first alphabetically.
6. If you find two different possible parent chains of the same length, you choose the one with more substituents coming off of it.

Notes

"parent chains"

Cyclic versions of alkanes are called cycloalkanes, and are named by the prefix used in the linear alkane with the same number of carbon atoms:

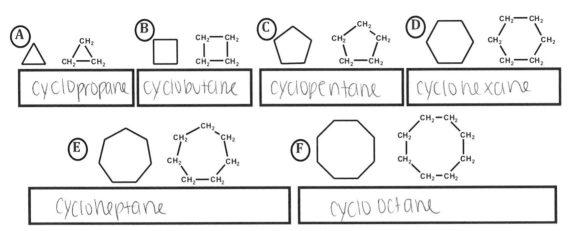

(A) cyclopropane   (B) cyclobutane   (C) cyclopentane   (D) cyclohexane

(E) cycloheptane   (F) cyclooctane

Of course, cycloalkanes can have substituents as well, and we need to know how to name substituted cycloalkanes.

Notes

Armed with our knowledge of naming branched alkanes, naming cycloalkanes is pretty straightforward. We can use the cycloalkane as the parent chain (if it is longest) and follow numbering/alphabetizing rules from there.

An additional rule for naming cycloalkanes:
If there is a possible parent chain on the cycloalkane that is longer than the # of carbons in the cycloalkane, use that as the parent chain, and name the cycloalkane as a substituent. For example:

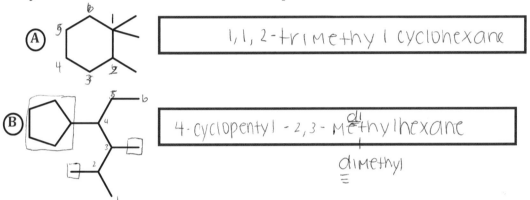

(A) 1,1,2-trimethyl cyclohexane

(B) 4-cyclopentyl-2,3-methylhexane

dimethyl

Notes

Depending on where we put the methyl substituents, we have two different **configurational isomers.**

same atoms, same connectivity, <u>but</u> groups pointing different in space... cannot interconvert w/o breaking bonds

A configurational isomer in which substituents are on the same side (both 'up' in this case) is referred to as a *cis-* isomer, while a configurational isomer with substituents on opposite sides is referred to as the *trans-* isomer.

cis - 1, 2, - dimethyl kyclohexane

trans - 1, 2 - dimethyl cyclohexane

Notes

For alkyl halides, name the compound using the rules for naming alkanes and cycloalkanes, and treat the halides as substituents:

CCl_2H_2 dichloromethane

1,2-dibromoethane

-F = Fluoro
-Cl = Chloro-
-Br = Bromo-
-I = Iodo-

trans-
1- Iodo-2-Methyl cyclohexane

1- Fluoro-3,4-dimethylpentane

Notes

For alcohols, use the rules for naming alkanes and cycloalkanes as a starting point, with the following adjustments:

1. replace the "e" at the end of the alkane name with "ol".

2. The alcohol is always given the lowest possible number. Note that this means that the alcohol is always given the "1" position in cycloalkanes (so, no need to add a number; we know it's always 1).

3. Place the number indicating the position of the alcohol directly before the parent chain name (which now ends in "ol").

Notes

CH_3OH Methanol

CH_3CH_2OH Ethanol

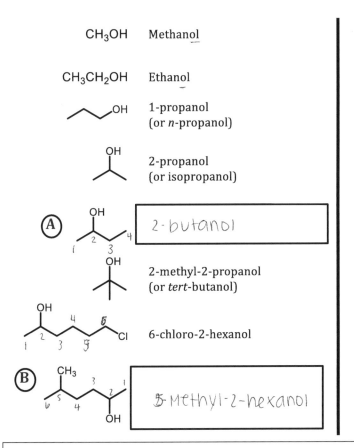

OH   1-propanol
        (or *n*-propanol)

OH   2-propanol
        (or isopropanol)

(A)   OH   2-butanol

        OH   2-methyl-2-propanol
               (or *tert*-butanol)

OH   6-chloro-2-hexanol

(B)   CH3   3-Methyl-2-hexanol

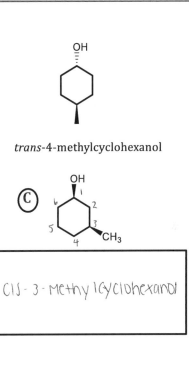

trans-4-methylcyclohexanol

(C)   OH

       cis-3-Methylcyclohexanol

Notes

We learned to classify carbocations as methyl, primary (1°), etc. We can classify alcohols/alkyl halides similarly.

$HO-CH_2R$

primary alcohol (1° alcohol)

secondary alcohol (2° alcohol)

tertiary alcohol (3° alcohol)

$X-CH_2R$

primary alkyl halide (1°)

secondary alkyl halide (2°)

tertiary alkyl halide (3°)

These classifications are very important, because the different classes of alcohols and alkyl halides have different reactivities, as we will learn in detail later in the course.

Notes 4 ethyl-
2,3-dimethylheptane

~~2 chloro~~
5-bromo-2-chloro-5ethyl-3,6-dimethyl heptane

5-fluoro-3 heptanol

propylcyclopentane

cis-1-bromo-3 methyl cyclohexane

6-ethyl-2,2,7-trimethyl-5-propyl nonane

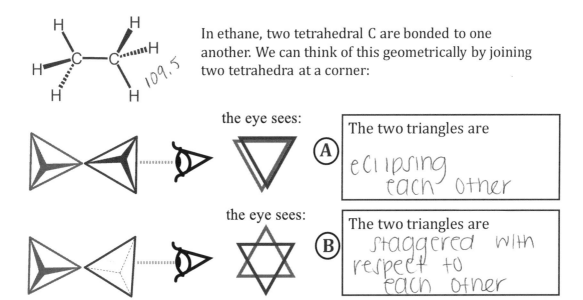

In ethane, two tetrahedral C are bonded to one another. We can think of this geometrically by joining two tetrahedra at a corner:

the eye sees:

(A) The two triangles are

eclipsing each other

the eye sees:

(B) The two triangles are

staggered with respect to each other

There are different **conformations** in which the two tetrahedra can be oriented with respect to one another, based on the relative rotation of the tetrahedral C atoms about the C–C bond.

Notes

The use of wedges and hashed lines lets us represent the possible 3D shapes so we can visualize the possible **conformations**:

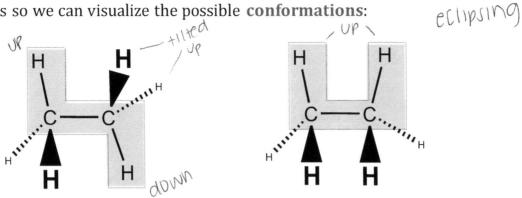

eclipsing

Notice in the left conformer the two H's coming out at us are far apart from one another, while in the right conformer they are right next to each other. These are two **conformational isomers -**

isomers that can be interconverted

Notes

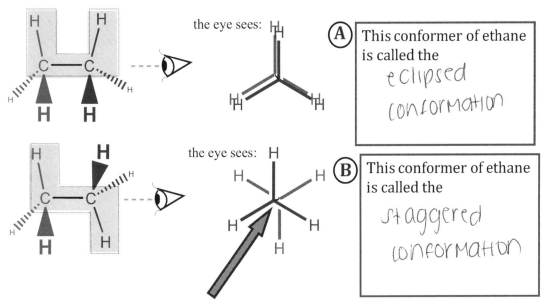

A | This conformer of ethane is called the

eclipsed conformation

B | This conformer of ethane is called the

staggered conformation

These representations emphasize the fact that we have two different conformers, but are a bit messy, especially at the middle, where all the bonds converge. For this reason, another way of representing this has been developed ...

Notes

Put a disk in to block the view of the middle portion of the back, so that the middle is more tidy, and you get what are called

(A) Newman Projections

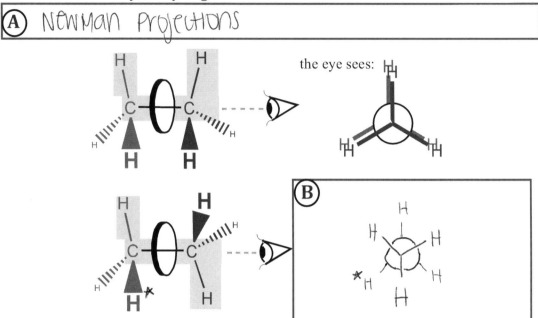

the eye sees:

(B)

If you cut a little circle of paper, put in on your model kit ethane, and look from the end, you'll see exactly what the Newman Projection represents.

Notes

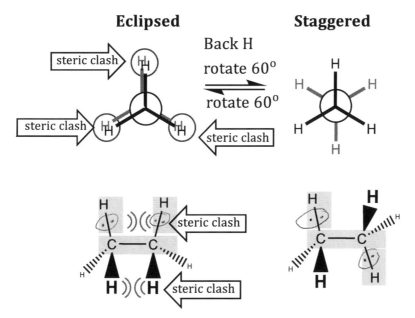

In the eclipsed conformation, H substituents are physically bumping into one another; such interactions are called **steric** interactions (steric interactions lead to different stereoisomers). In staggered, the H atoms are far apart. Because of sterics,

staggered is more stable

Notes

Steric clashes leads to an energy barrier (E_a) to rotation about the C-C bond.
This energy barrier is called the **torsional strain** (resistance to twisting).
Below is an energy profile showing how stability changes with bond rotation.

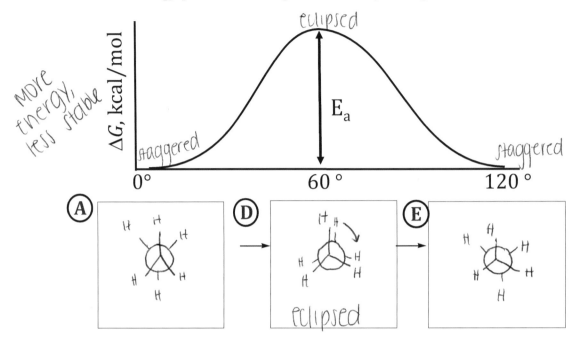

Notes

Ethane is simple because we only have hydrogens on the C-C bond. Now we look at a more complicated example, butane.

H_3C — CH_3

Butane has both hydrogen and methyl groups attached to the C2-C3 bond. This leads to more possible stereoisomers than we saw with ethane ...

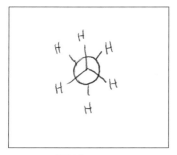

Ethane

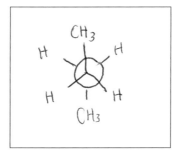

Butane

Notes

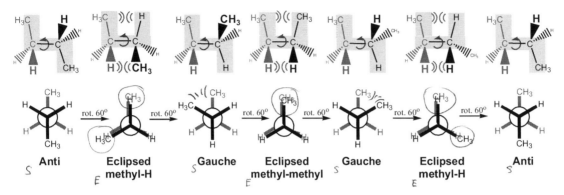

<u>four distinct conformers:</u>

1. Anti   2. Gauche   3. Eclipsed methy-H   4. Eclipsed methyl-methyl

We can predict the relative stability of these conformations by evaluating the steric strain in each of them...

Notes

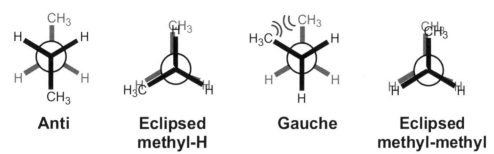

Anti   **Eclipsed**   **Gauche**   **Eclipsed**
              methyl-H   **methyl-methyl**

Since methyl groups are larger than hydrogens,

Ⓐ eclipsed methyl-methyl has more
destabilizing repulsion than does
   eclipsed methyl-H

In fact, two methyl groups have some steric repulsion even when they
are still 60° apart from one another, a repulsion called a

Ⓑ Gauche interaction; not as repulsive as
eclipsing interactions, however gauche is less
      stable than anti

Notes

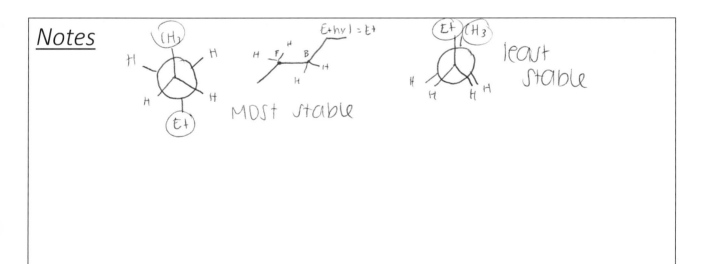

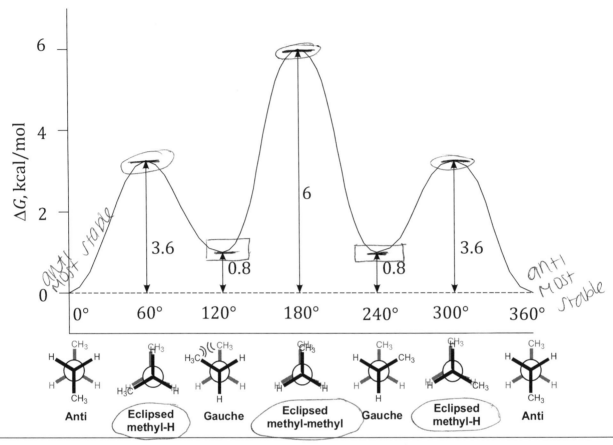

Notes

We have discussed steric strain (including torsional strain) in linear alkanes.

One additional consideration for cyclic compounds is **angle strain**. Cycloalkanes are made of sp^3 hybridized carbons, which favor bond angles of 109.5°. However, this differs from the angles in some regular polygons:

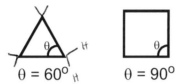

$\theta = 60°$ $\theta = 90°$ $\theta = 108°$

The difference between ideal and actual angle leads to **angle strain**. We consider this as part of the overall **Ring strain:**

combination of angle strain + steric (eclipsing) strain

Notes

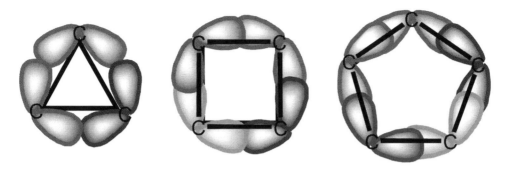

An **origin of angle strain**

Now we consider the other contributors to ring strain: steric interactions
(and torsional strain)

Notes

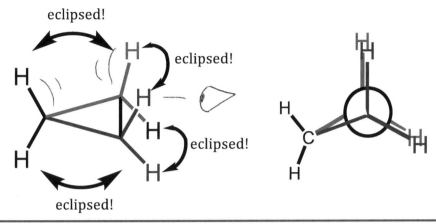

In addition to lots of **angle strain**, cyclopropane also has

All H atoms eclipsing!

The total **ring strain** is about 30 kcal/mol (10 kcal per methylene).

Notes

Planar   **Puckered**

All eclipsing!   Not eclipsing.
C-C-C angle: C-C-C angle:
     90°   88°

In addition to **angle strain**, planar cyclobutane has H's eclipsed. **Molecules will always** distort to alleviate repulsion (get more stable if possible)

Cyclobutane twists ("puckers"), increasing the angle strain a bit, but relieving all of the eclipsing torsional strain. The puckered form, on the right, is the favored form. The total **ring strain** is about 28 kcal/mol (7 kcal per methylene).

Notes

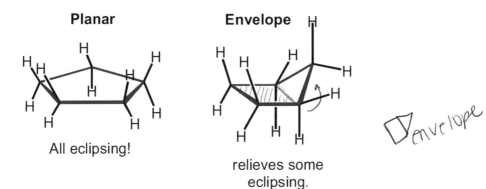

Planar

Envelope

All eclipsing!

relieves some
eclipsing.

envelope

In addition to some **angle strain**, planar cyclopentane also has

(A) - all H atoms eclipsed

Cyclopentane undergoes a distortion to the **envelope form**, relieving some of
the eclipsing torsional strain, so:

(B) envelope is more stable conformation

The total **ring strain** is about 10 kcal/mol (2 kcal per methylene).

Notes

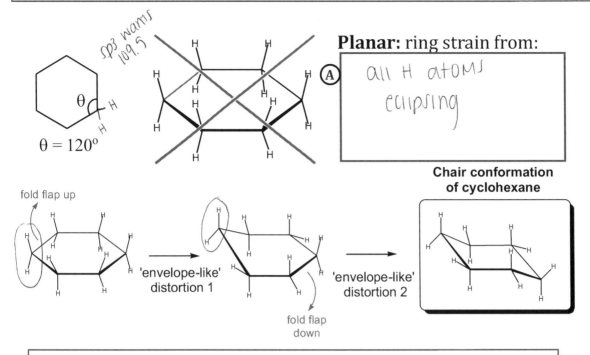

$\theta = 120°$

sp3 wants 109.5

Planar: ring strain from:

(A) all H atoms eclipsing

fold flap up

'envelope-like' distortion 1

'envelope-like' distortion 2

fold flap down

Chair conformation of cyclohexane

Ring strain in the Chair Conformation:

approximately zero

We will now study why this is the case.

Notes

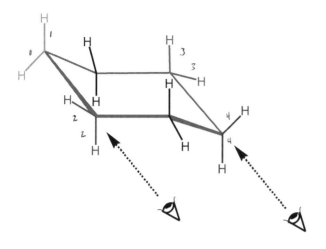

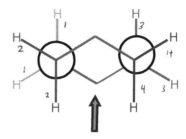

All staggered.

This picture shows two Newman Projections; one projection down the right side and one down the left side of cyclohexane (indicated by the eyes). Build a model to see this more easily.

The chair conformation features

1. no angle strain

2. all H atoms staggered

This is **why the chair conformation is very stable**.

Notes

There are two distinct types of hydrogen atoms in cyclohexane. It is very important to understand the difference between these two types.

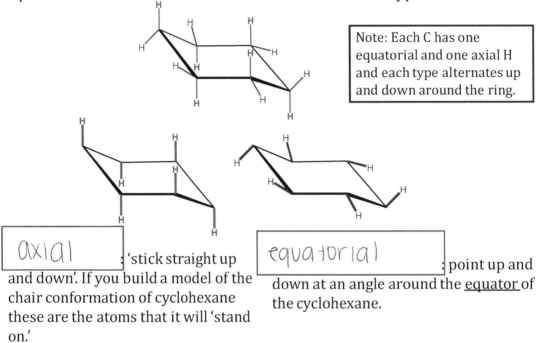

Note: Each C has one equatorial and one axial H and each type alternates up and down around the ring.

axial: 'stick straight up and down'. If you build a model of the chair conformation of cyclohexane these are the atoms that it will 'stand on.'

equatorial: point up and down at an angle around the <u>equator</u> of the cyclohexane.

Notes

102

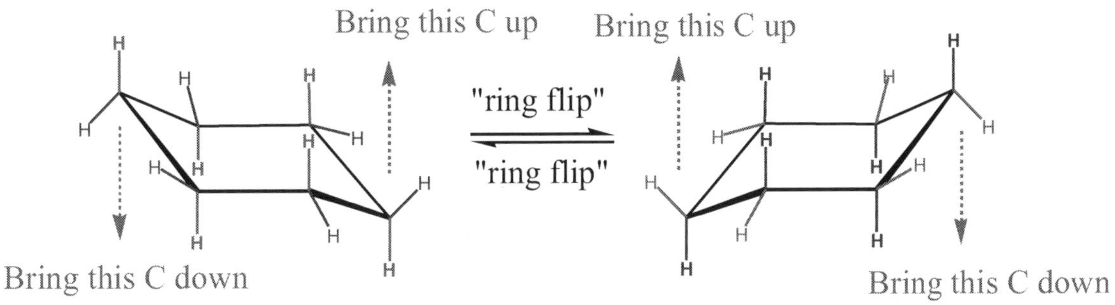

Bring this C up   Bring this C up

"ring flip"

"ring flip"

Bring this C down

Bring this C down

A **ring flip** involves distorting the cyclohexane ring so that the 'up' flap moves to the 'down' position and vice versa.

A **ring flip** switches:

Notes

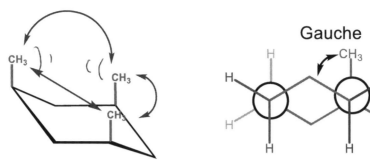

Gauche

Substituents may cause steric strains. Axial methyl (or larger) groups can clash with other axial substituents on the same face of the ring. This type of steric interaction is called a

(A) 1,3- diaxial repulsion

Equatorial positions do not have these interactions, so

(B) Conformations in which larger groups are equatorial are more stable than those in which larger groups are in axial position

Notes

104

Problem: For each, draw the most stable conformational isomer

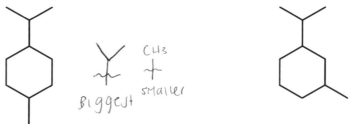

CH3

Biggest   SMaller

1-isopropyl-4-methylcyclohexane   1-isopropyl-3-methylcyclohexane

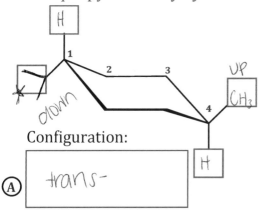

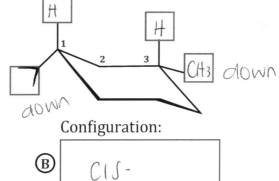

Configuration:

Ⓐ   trans-

Configuration:

Ⓑ   cis-

Notes

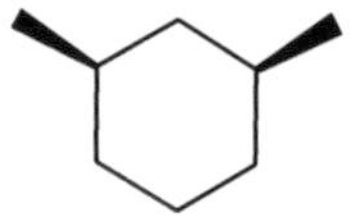

cis-1,3-dimethycyclohexane

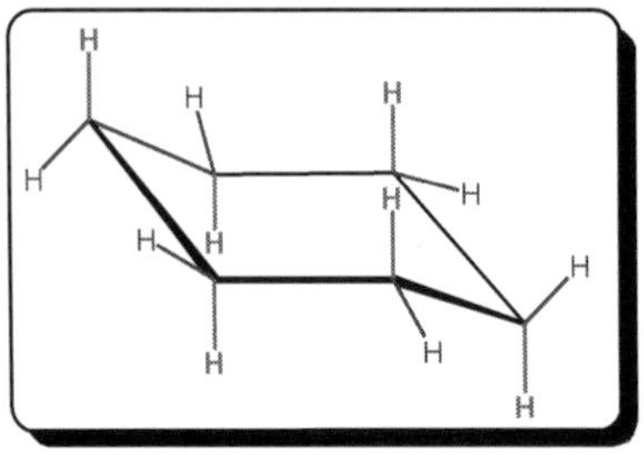

For Reference

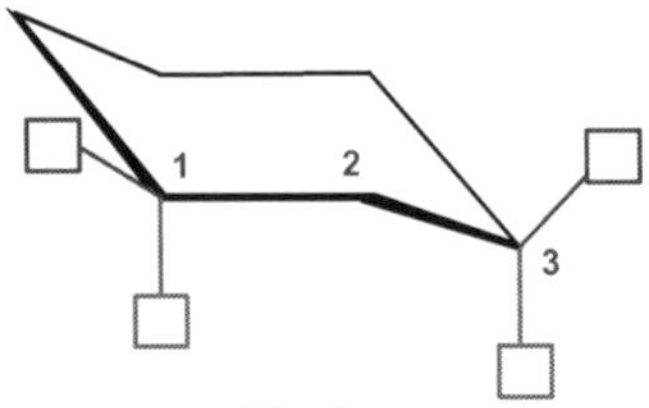

Choices

both CIS

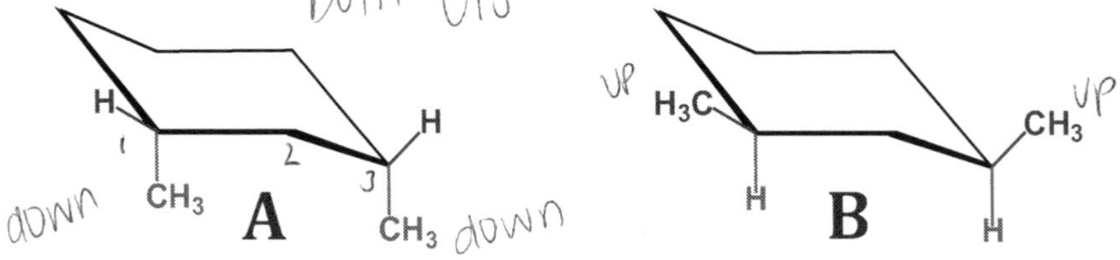

A

down   CH₃   CH₃ down

UP   H₃C   CH₃ UP

B

Both A & B are correct for CIS
B is more stable b/c equatorial methyls

Notes   trans-1-Ethyl-2-Methyl cyclohexane

Et

CH₃   Ethyl down
        Methyl has to be up

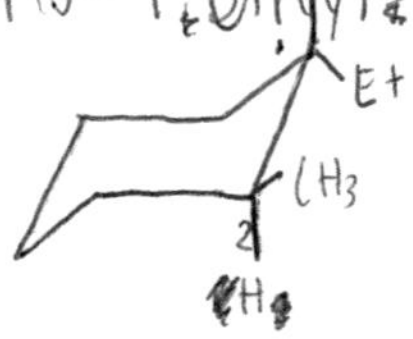

CH₃

★ MOre stable
   both
   equatorial

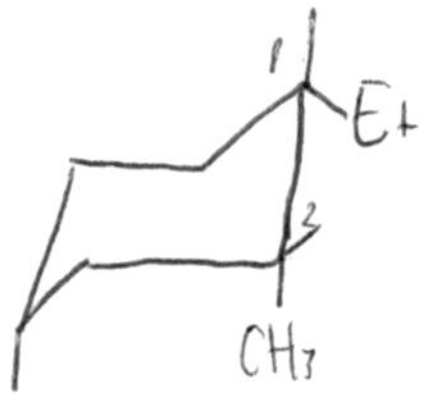

Et   Ethyl and
      Methyl both down

CH₃

cis-1-ethyl-2-Methylcyclohexane

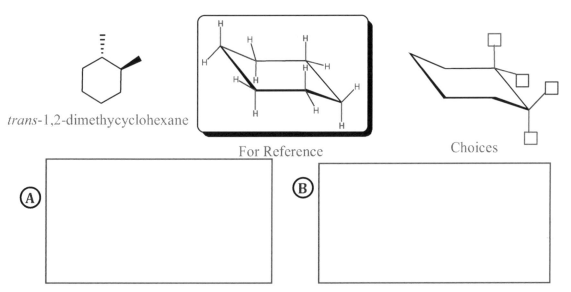

trans-1,2-dimethycyclohexane

For Reference

Choices

(A)

(B)

Axial methyls will have strong 1,3-diaxial repulsion, so this form will be unfavorable. The most stable form is therefore:

(C)

Notes

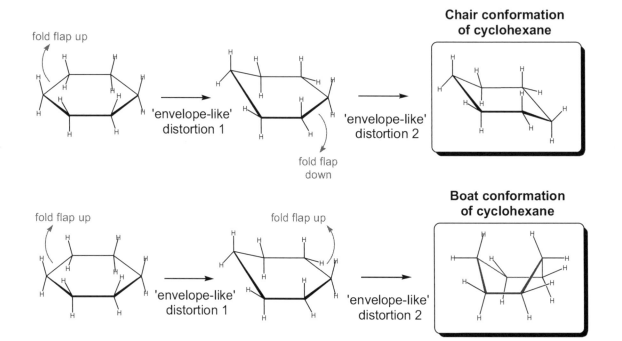

Chair conformation
of cyclohexane

Boat conformation
of cyclohexane

Notes

Steric interaction
(known as a **"flagpole" interaction**)

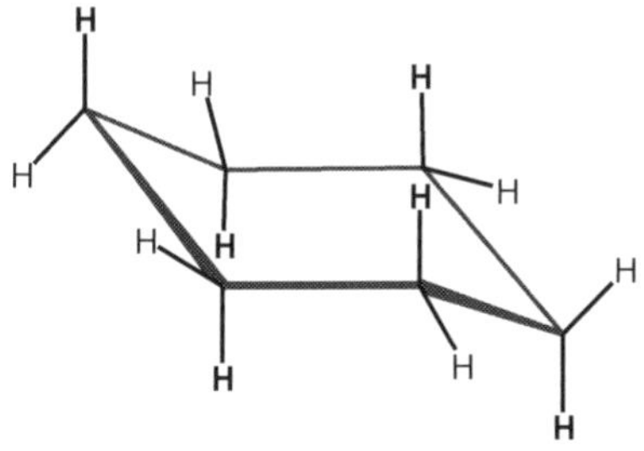

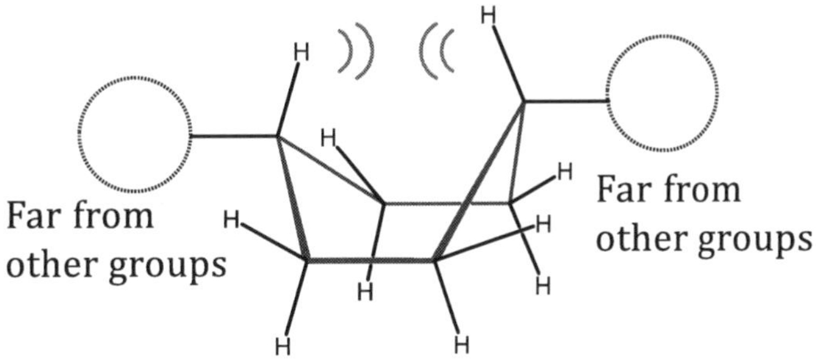

Far from
other groups

Far from
other groups

"**chair**" conformation is very stable:
  - no eclipsing interactions
  - angles favorable
  - Generally preferred

"**boat**" conformation
  - eclipsing interactions
  - steric strain
  - angles strained

Boat only preferred when:

Notes

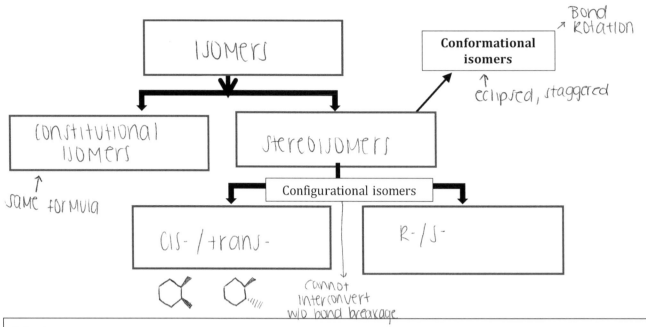

Conformational isomers → Bond Rotation

↑ eclipsed, staggered

constitutional isomers
↑ same formula

cannot interconvert w/o bond breakage.

Notes

Stereoisomers:

 Same atom connectivity; different 3-D shape

Conformational stereoisomers:

 Can interconvert by bond rotation

- staggered and eclipsed conformers
- *gauche* and *anti* conformers
- Chair or boat chair conformers of cyclohexane

Configurational stereoisomers:

Ⓒ Must break at least one bond to interconvert

NOW:

enantiomers:

Ⓓ Mirror images that are not the same (nonsuperimposable)

diastereomers:

Ⓔ not mirror images and not the same (nonsuperimposable)

Notes

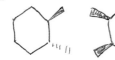

diastereomers

Molecules with "handedness" possess ⒜ chirality

and are ⒝ chiral

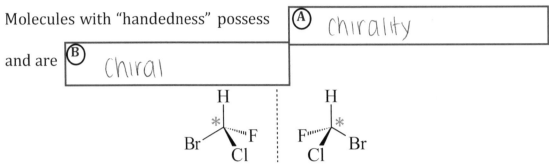

These are nonsuperimposable mirror images; using definitions on the previous slide, this is a pair of **enantiomers** ("left- and right-handed" isomers). The molecule is chiral and possesses a **chiral (stereogenic) center** (also called a **stereocenter**). These centers can be labeled with asterisks for clarity.

⒞ These two are mirror images but they are not identical ~~isomers~~

Notes

(A) For a carbon atom to be a stereocenter it must:

have 4 different
    groups bound
        to it

- chiral center
- stereocenter
- stereogenic center

(B) the stereocenters are marked with asteriks. Note that one of the 4 different groups is a hydrogen that happens to not be drawn in the bond line representation

A molecule WITHOUT a stereocenter is

(C) achiral

If the molecule has a **plane of symmetry** it is

(D) a chiral

A molecule with a stereocenter **and** a plane of symmetry is achiral.

(E) example:

line shows symmetry

Such compounds are called **meso** compounds.

Notes

symmetry > meso
achiral   compound

Mark the stereocenters with asterisks.

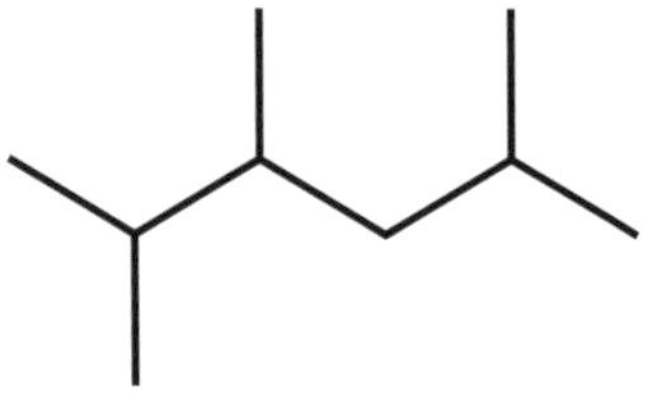

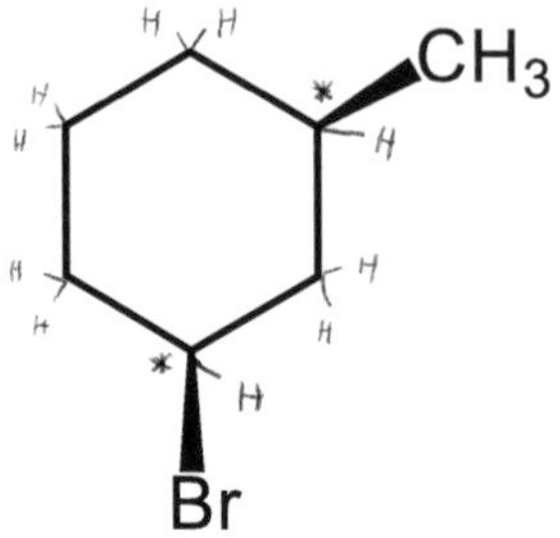

CH3

Br

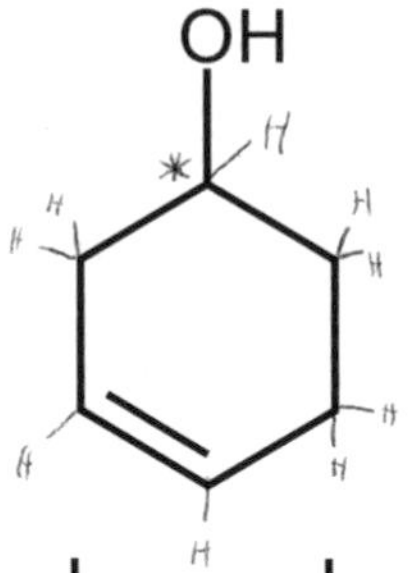

OH

cannot be
  chiral if:
- two H's
- only 3
    groups

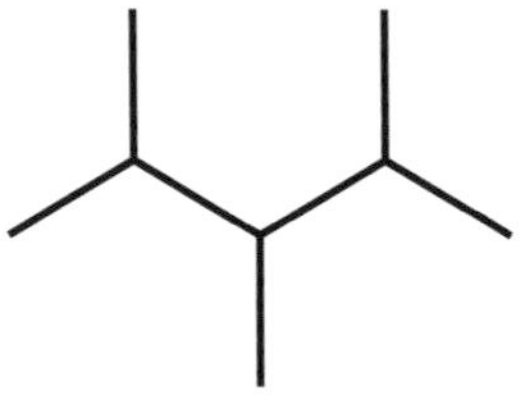

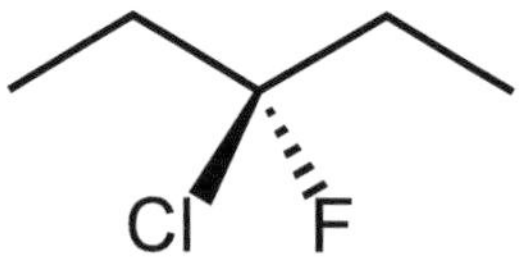

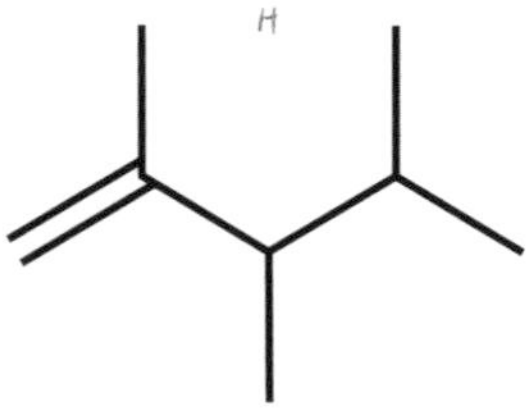

Notes

Many physical properties of enantiomers are **IDENTICAL**

(A)   B.P.   Melting point, boiling point,
        M.P.   solubility, stability

Two Enantiomers can interact very differently with other chiral molecules. **This is especially important in biological systems!**
1. Amino acids

(B)   only one enantiomer provided the vast
            majority of naturally

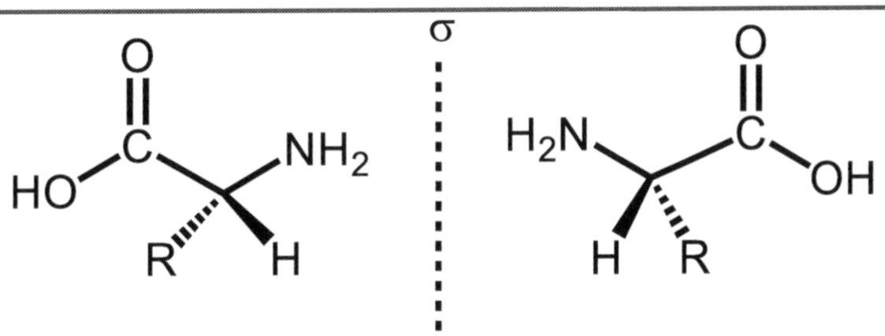

σ

Notes

2. Enzymes/cellular signaling

(A)

only one enantiomer
May bind a particular
    receptor or rxn site

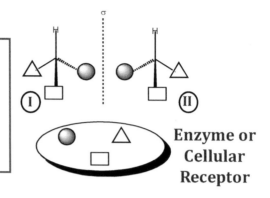

Enzyme or Cellular Receptor

3. Drugs

(B)

for some drugs (notably thalidomide)
one isomer has a
    beneficial activity,
the other can be hazardous

Notes

If many physical properties are identical, we use to distinguish two enantiomers?

(A) polarimetry - measures the rotation of plane polarized light

 d-
(+)-

 l-
(-)-

(B) sample causes clockwise rotation: dextrorotatory d-

(C) sample causes counterclockwise rotation: levorotatory l-

(D) sample is not optically active

Notes

light vector coming in

sample with one enantiomer

light vector after passing through

Optically inactive:

(A)

Optically pure: (C)

Optical purity: (B)

(a sample with 80% enantiomer '**X**' and 20% enantiomer '**Y**' has 60% e.e. or 60% optical purity)

Notes

SKIP

Enantiomers of different compounds rotate light by different amounts, so an optically pure compound has a characteristic specific rotation [α]. Two enantiomers of the same compound have **specific rotations** with the same magnitude but in opposite directions. The equation used to calculate the specific rotation is:

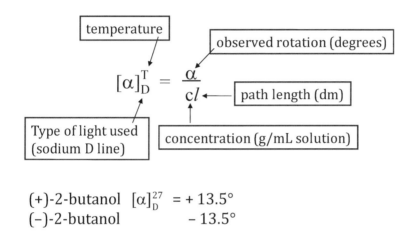

temperature

observed rotation (degrees)

$$[\alpha]_D^T = \frac{\alpha}{cl}$$

path length (dm)

Type of light used (sodium D line)

concentration (g/mL solution)

(+)-2-butanol $[\alpha]_D^{27} = +13.5°$
(−)-2-butanol $-13.5°$

Notes

119

SKIP

We obviously need a convention to designate the absolute configuration of a given molecule. (R or S)

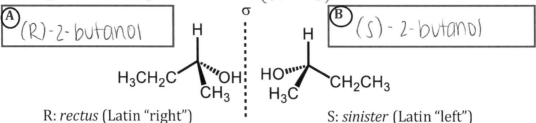

Ⓐ (R)-2-butanol

Ⓑ (S) - 2- butanol

R: *rectus* (Latin "right")   S: *sinister* (Latin "left")

Whether the configuration of a chiral center is *R* or *S* depends only on

Ⓒ The 3D arrangements of groups

and is **NOT** determined by

Ⓓ direction of light rotation (a "d-" molecule may be R- or S-)

So, we need a convention for assigning "priority" to the units that are attached to a chiral atom ...

Notes

Priority Rules:

1. First look at atom directly attached to the stereogenic atom

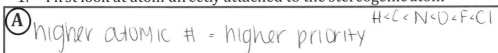

A higher atomic # = higher priority $H < C < N < O < F < Cl$

2. If same atomic number, higher mass = higher priority (D > H, $^{13}C > ^{12}C$, etc.)

3. If atoms A and B are identical, move to highest priority atom attached to A and B until a break in the tie is found (first compare A1 to B1 priority. If tie, compare A2 to B2. If tie, compare A3 to B3, etc.)

4. For Example:

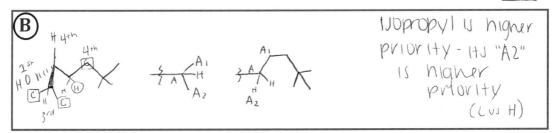

B

H 4th

Isopropyl is higher priority - its "A2" is higher priority (C vs H)

Notes

4. If a substituent is doubly or triply bonded to another atom, use the 'break and duplicate' strategy to create 'false atoms' as a visual aid to prioritize:

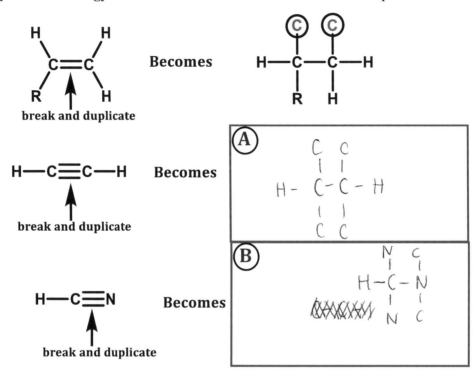

Becomes

break and duplicate

Notes

1. (A) assign priorities to the four groups
   (using CIP rules)
2. Point the **lowest** priority group away from you

3. Determine the direction of procession from **1-2-3** priorities:

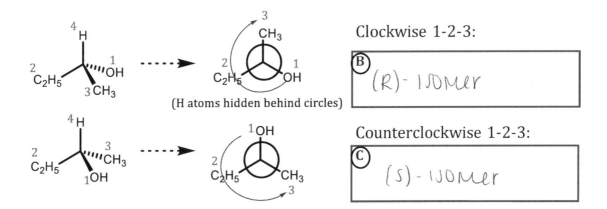

(H atoms hidden behind circles)

Clockwise 1-2-3:

(B) (R)- ISOMer

Counterclockwise 1-2-3:

(C) (S)- ISOMer

Notes

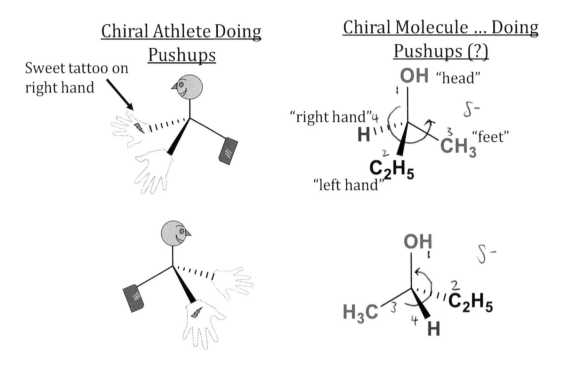

Chiral Athlete Doing Pushups

Sweet tattoo on right hand

Chiral Molecule ... Doing Pushups (?)

OH "head"

"right hand" 4 — H

$\delta-$

"feet" 3 — CH_3

2 — C_2H_5 "left hand"

OH

$\delta-$

H_3C — 3 — 2 — C_2H_5

4 — H

We need a way to visualize rotation of a chiral molecule without losing stereochemical information

Notes

4 H

Et 2

HO 1

CH₃ 3

Et 4 O

HO

CH₃

H 4

Et 2

CH₃ 3

1 OH

$\delta-$

There are Many Ways to Draw a Chiral Object

Hand-Stand

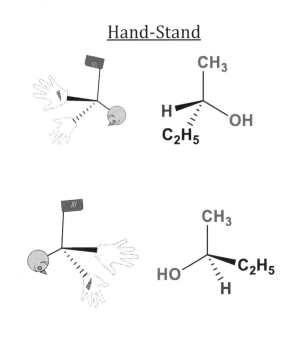

$$CH_3$$
$$H \quad \quad OH$$
$$C_2H_5$$

$$CH_3$$
$$HO \quad \quad C_2H_5$$
$$H$$

Ceiling Pushup!

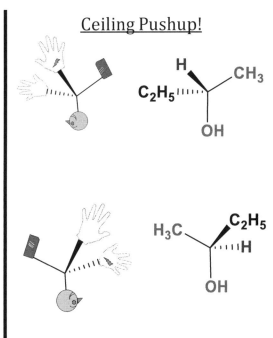

$$H \quad \quad CH_3$$
$$C_2H_5 \quad \quad OH$$

$$C_2H_5$$
$$H_3C \quad \quad H$$
$$OH$$

Notes

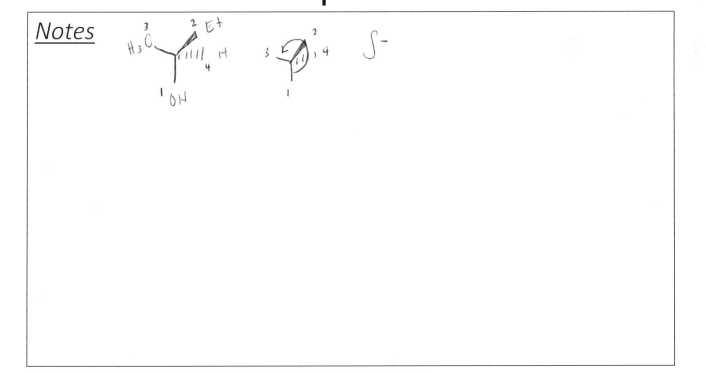

$$H_3\overset{3}{C} \quad \overset{2}{Et}$$
$$\quad \quad H^4$$
$$\overset{1}{OH}$$

$$\overset{3}{} \quad \overset{2}{} \quad {}_4$$
$$\overset{1}{}$$

$$S-$$

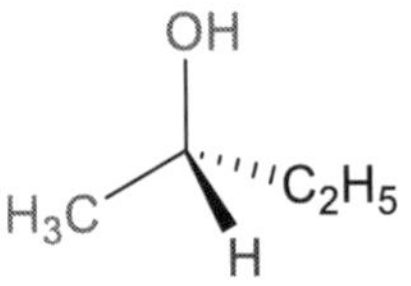

OH
H₃C‑‑‑‑C₂H₅
H

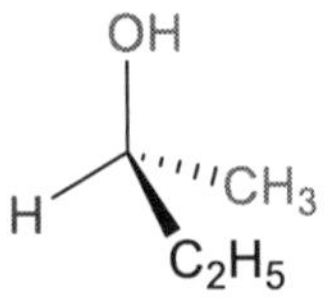

OH
H‑‑‑CH₃
C₂H₅

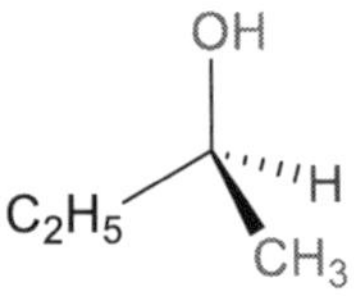

OH
C₂H₅‑‑‑H
CH₃

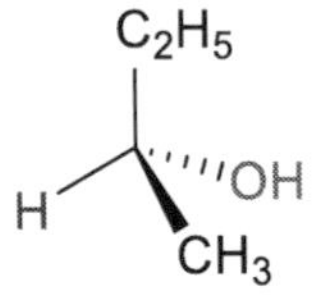

(A) Two other ways:

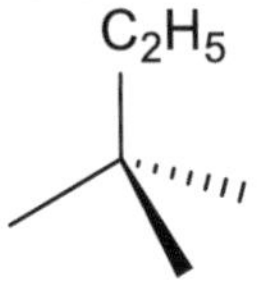

C₂H₅

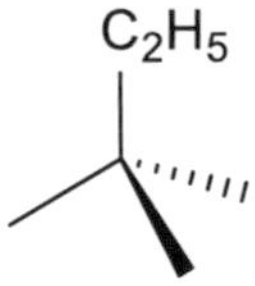

C₂H₅

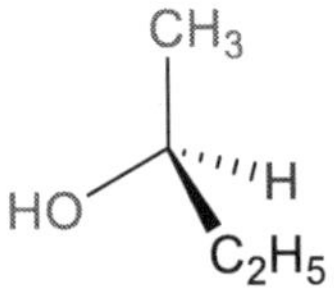

C₂H₅
H‑‑‑OH
CH₃

CH₃
HO‑‑‑H
C₂H₅

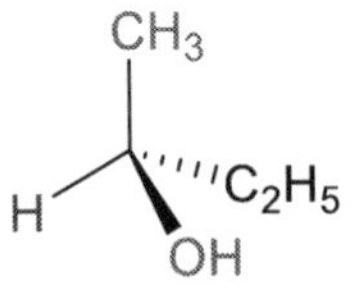

CH₃
H‑‑‑C₂H₅
OH

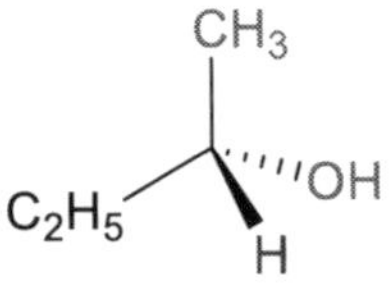

CH₃
C₂H₅‑‑‑OH
H

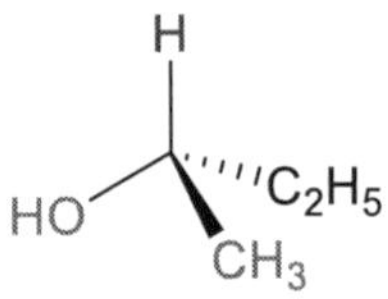

(B) Two other ways:

H

H

H
HO‑‑‑C₂H₅
CH₃

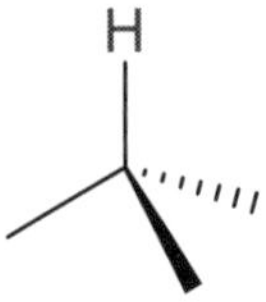

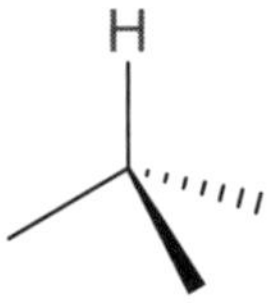

Notes

In addition to standard dash-wedge notation, a **Fischer projection** can show 3D shape.

In a Fischer projection, horizontal lines: (A)

Vertical lines: (B)

Fischer
Projection

$$H—\overset{\overset{\displaystyle OH}{|}}{\underset{\underset{\displaystyle CH_3}{|}}{C}}—C_2H_5 \;=\; H—\overset{\overset{\displaystyle OH}{\vdots}}{\underset{\underset{\displaystyle CH_3}{\vdots}}{C}}—C_2H_5 \;=\;$$

$$H_3C—\overset{OH}{\underset{H}{C}}'''C_2H_5$$

(One of many ways to draw it)

Coming in for a hug but leaning away
(tattoo on palm as well apparently)

Notes

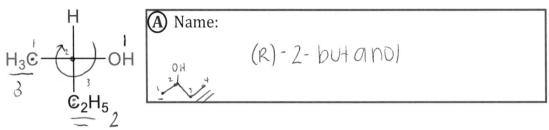

(A) Name:

(R)-2-butanol

Convert to wedge and dash structure (several correct representations):

(B)

Fischer Projection and Wedge/Hashed Lines for (R)-3-methylheptane:

(C)

Notes

I	II	III	IV
S	R	S	R
R	S	S	R

enant.
all
change

enant.
all
change

any other pair
is a
diastereomer

Diastereomers:

Ⓐ not same, not mirror images
        (stereoisomers)
A compound with 'n' chiral centers can have up to 2^n stereoisomers.

Consider 3-chloro-2-butanol, which has Stereocenters at C2 and C3:

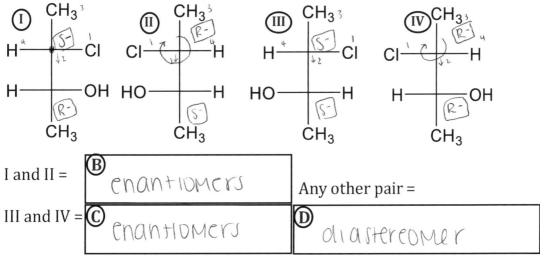

I and II = Ⓑ enantiomers

III and IV = Ⓒ enantiomers

Any other pair = Ⓓ diastereomer

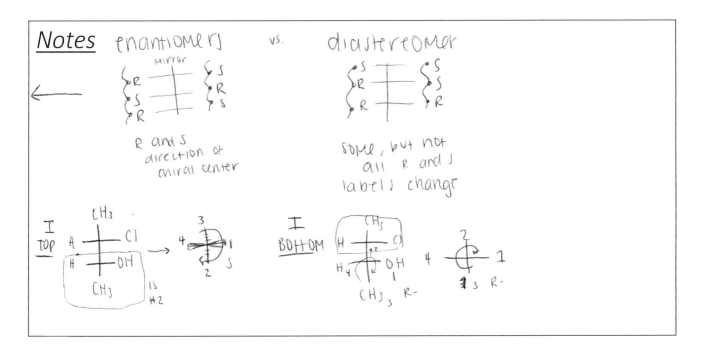

Meso Compounds:

Ⓐ chiral atoms ≠ plane of symmetry, so achiral

So compounds I and II are ACHIRAL!

Consider 2,3-dichlorobutanol, which has Stereocenters at C2 and C3:

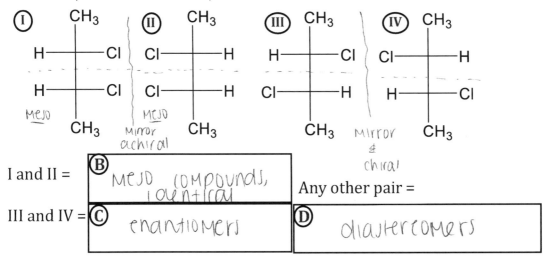

I and II = Ⓑ MESO compounds, identical

III and IV = Ⓒ enantiomers

Any other pair = Ⓓ diastereomers

Notes

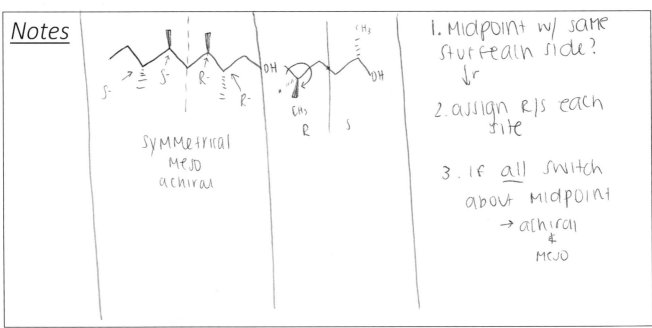

1. Midpoint w/ same stuff each side?
   ↓r

2. assign R/s each site

3. If all switch about midpoint
   → achiral & MESO

BACK

Stereocenters may be generated, eliminated or changed in the course of a given reaction on the basis of the mechanism involved in the reaction.

A couple of overarching concepts can help keep track of Stereocenters in a reactions:

1. If reagents/reactants are achiral, then:

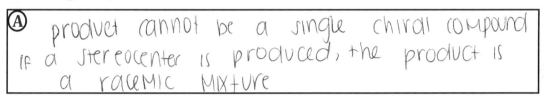

(A) product cannot be a single chiral compound
If a stereocenter is produced, the product is
a racemic mixture

2. If reagents/reactants are chiral, then:

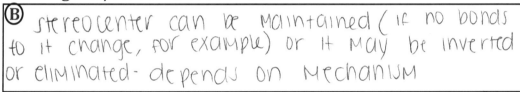

(B) stereocenter can be maintained (if no bonds
to it change, for example) or it may be inverted
or eliminated- depends on mechanism

Notes

achiral ⟶

[Reaction box with carbocation structure]

Br^-
coordination

?

[Product structure with Br]

(A)

Br — [structure] C_2H_5
CH₃

R-isomer

Br^-
Path I

[Central carbocation structure]
H₃C⁽⁺⁾ C_2H_5
Achiral Reactants!

Br^-
Path II

(B)

CH_3 [structure] Br
C_2H_5

S-isomer

The steric barrier to coordination from either face is the same. The two enantiomers have equal stability. So the product is a:

(C)

racemic mixture

We will apply our knowledge of these general principles to other reactions as we encounter them.

Notes

132

Nucleophilicity is a measure of how rapidly a compound (a nucleophile) will attack an electron-deficient atom

Nucleophilicity is measured by a rate constant (k).

(A) The rate constant depends only on the activation energy (height of barrier to rxn) needed to reach the transition state in the rate-limiting step

Basicity is a measure of how favorable it is for a compound (a base) to shares its lone pair, often with a proton.

Basicity is measured by the acid dissociation constant (K_a).

(B) The equilibrium constant depends only on the difference in thermodynamic stability (Gibbs free energy) of the starting material(s) and product(s)

Notes

133

Nucleophilicity Trends

(A) More negative = Better Nucleophile (Nu)

    $O^{2-} > HO^- > H_2O$

    $RO^- > ROH$

    $HS^- > H_2S$

(B) less electronegative in a row atom w/$\ominus$ = better Nu

    $H_2N^- > HO^- > F^-$

    $H_3N > H_2O$

    $RO^- > RCO_2^-$

(C) in a column,

bigger = more Nu

    $I^- > Br^- > Cl^- > F^-$

    $HS^- > HO^-$

    $PH_3 > NH_3$

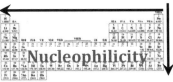

Nucleophilicity

Notes

134

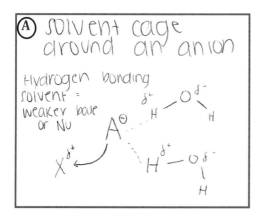

A) solvent cage around an anion

Hydrogen bonding solvent = weaker base or Nu

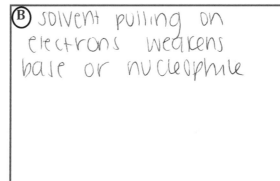

B) solvent pulling on electrons weakens base or nucleophile

It is easier to break the ion-dipole interactions between a weak base and the solvent than between a strong base and the solvent

C) 1) base/Nu strength is weaker the stronger the IMF of the solvent

2) the effect is greater for stronger bases

Notes

Solvents can be classified into several types on the basis of the type of intermolecular forces they can exhibit with other molecules:

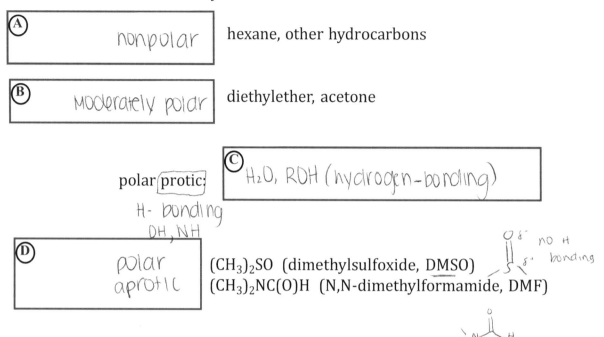

(A) nonpolar   hexane, other hydrocarbons

(B) moderately polar   diethylether, acetone

polar protic   (C) H_2O, ROH (hydrogen-bonding)
    H- bonding
    OH, NH

(D) polar aprotic $(CH_3)_2SO$ (dimethylsulfoxide, DMSO)
    $(CH_3)_2NC(O)H$ (N,N-dimethylformamide, DMF)

no H bonding

Notes

OH⁻ in H_2O: strong ion-dipole interaction with water diminishes its
              nucleophilicity (less reactive; higher E_a)
    in DMSO: weaker solvation and thus more nucleophilic (faster
              reaction) versus the same reaction in water

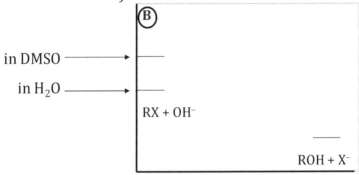

Notes

Alkyl Halides react with even poor nucleophiles, often solvents such as water or alcohols, to yield alcohols or ethers:

$$\text{H-OH} + \text{R-X} \longrightarrow \text{R-OH} + \text{H}^+ + \text{X}^-$$
$$\text{H-OR'} + \text{R-X} \longrightarrow \text{R-OR'} + \text{H}^+ + \text{X}^-$$

X = Cl, Br, or I

This is a **substitution reaction**, and it proceeds by a specific mechanism called the **S$_N$1** mechanism. This is an abbreviation meant to help you remember how the reaction takes place:

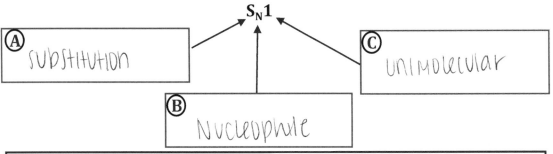

S$_N$1

Ⓐ substitution

Ⓑ Nucleophile

Ⓒ unimolecular

Because the substrate (RX) reacts with the solvent, this reaction is sometimes called **solvolysis** as well.

Notes

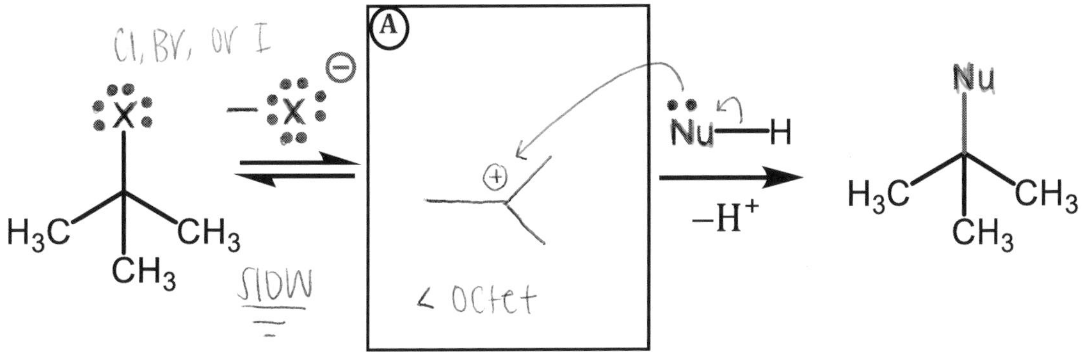

CI, BY, or I

< octet

SIOW

S_N1 is a two-step sequence of steps:

    1)   Heterolysis (lose a good **Leaving Group (LG)**)

    2)   Coordination (of a Nucleophile)

Heterolysis occurs: (B) If x = good leaving group &
enough heat is added

A "good" leaving group
(LG) is: (C) neutral or a stable anion
after heterolysis

Notes

1) heterolysis

2) coordination

(with loss of proton)

SLOW

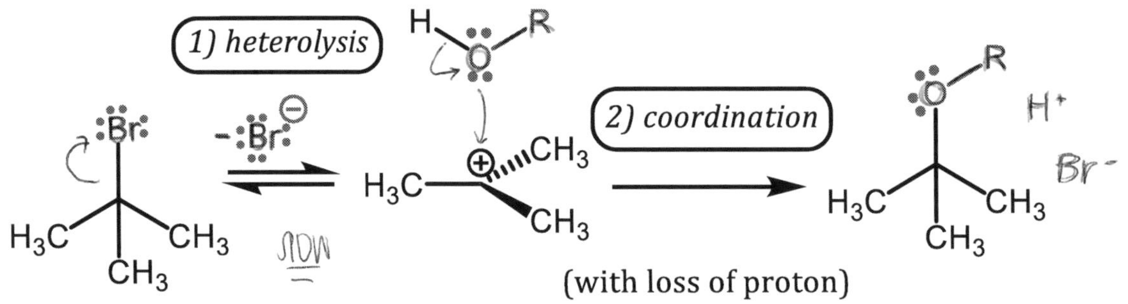

S$_N$1 = 1) Heterolysis, 2) Coordination. **Fill in the curved arrows to show the flow of electrons**

R in HOR can be: Ⓐ H or a hydrocarbon chain

Rate-Limiting Step: Ⓑ heterolysis to form carbocation

Rate Law: Ⓒ rate = k[R-LG]   S$_N$1

one species

Notes

Rate-Limiting Step for S$_N$1

Carbocation
(sp^2)

The rate-limiting step leads to a leaving group (here X-) and a carbocation as products. Substrates that produce more stable products react faster by S$_N$1.

Substrate trend:

$CH_3X < 1° RX$ < 2° < 3°

Too unstable; will not work for S$_N$1!

REACTIVITY →

Leaving group (LG) trend:

R-F < R-Cl < R-Br < R-I

Generally difficult for S$_N$1!

More stable anion
faster rxn

Notes

fastest?

X 1°

2° $\xrightarrow[\text{H}_2\text{O}]{\Delta}$

3°   fastest

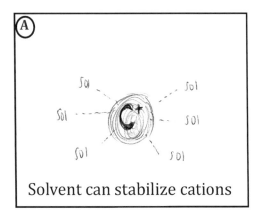

Solvent can stabilize cations

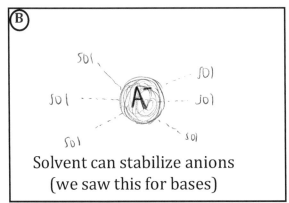

Solvent can stabilize anions
(we saw this for bases)

Stronger attractive intermolecular forces are more stabilizing, so the solvents in which the S$_N$1 reaction is the fastest are:

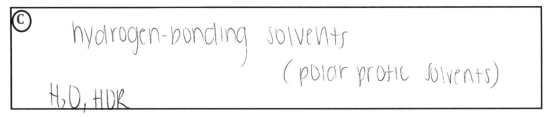

hydrogen-bonding solvents
                    (polar protic solvents)
H$_2$O, HOR

Notes

Thermodynamically favorable reactions will occur spontaneously when they are kinetically and mechanistically accessible. In **Lecture Topic I.8** we saw that carbocations can rearrange.

Carbocations will always

Ⓐ rearrange if doing so makes them more stable

The rate at which the carbocation rearranges is:

Ⓑ >> faster than rxn of C⁺ w/ external species

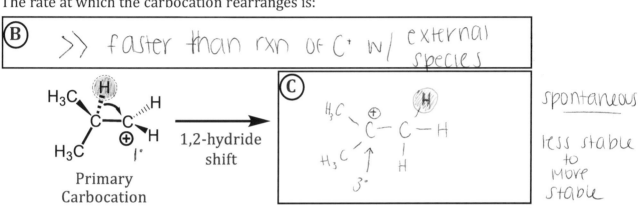

Primary Carbocation

1,2-hydride shift

Ⓒ 3°

spontaneous

less stable to more stable

Notes

Alkyl groups can also migrate to create a more stable species. This *usually* only happens when there are no hydride units to shift. A notable exception is when rearrangement leads to relief of ring strain (given as an Example in the Reaction Guide).

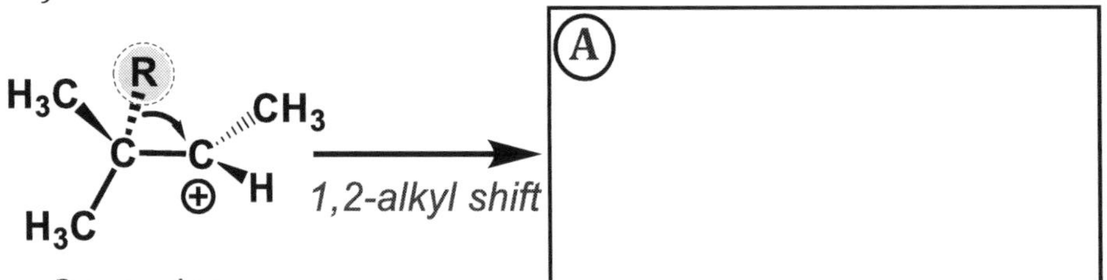

Secondary
Carbocation

1,2-alkyl shift

(A)

Because a carbocation forms as an intermediate in the S_N1 reaction:

(B)

Notes

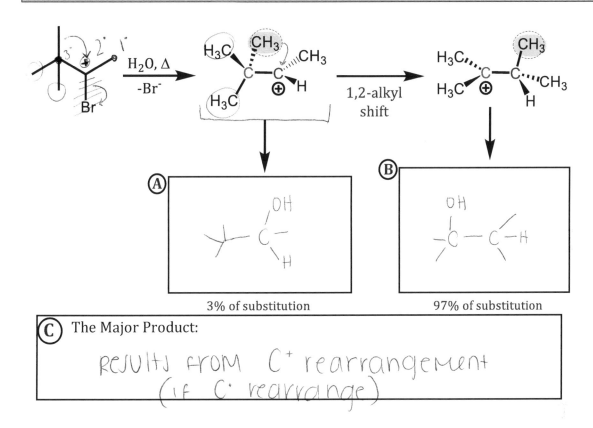

(A) 3% of substitution

(B) 97% of substitution

(C) The Major Product:

REJULTJ FROM C⁺ rearrangement
    (if C· rearrange)

Notes

145

We learned the general form of the S$_N$2 reaction in **Lecture Topic 1.8**. We will now study this mechanistic step is more detail.

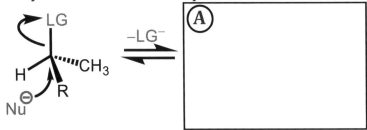

(B) Unlike the S$_N$1 reaction, the S$_N$2 reaction occurs in a single step. This type of reaction is called a:

(C) That there is only one step means that Nu, substrate and leaving group all influence rate. The rate law is:

Like S$_N$1, then, more stable LG = faster reaction rate

Notes [S$_N$1]

SLOW → Nu$^{\ominus}$ → Nu

X$^-$(LG)

• More stable LG = faster
• More stable C$^+$ = faster

(polar protic) • H-bonding solvent = faster
↓

X$^-$ ----- H$-$O, H

H, O, H

Lecture Topic II.4: The S$_N$2 Mechanism
S$_N$2 Requires a "Good" Nucleophile

In S$_N$1, the nucleophile attacks a cation, which has a strong enough pull on electrons to pull in even poor nucleophiles. In S$_N$2, the nucleophile attacks a neutral compound, which has a significantly lower attraction for a nucleophile than does a cation. For this reason:

(A)

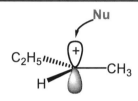

Nucleophilic attack in the coordination step of the S$_N$1 mechanism

Nucleophilic attack in the concerted S$_N$2 mechanism

(B) The better the Nucleophile:

Notes [S N 2]

- More stable LG = faster
- less bulky substrate = faster
  (R – X)
- ~~xxxxxx~~ better Nucleophile = faster
- polar aprotic solvent = faster
  (DMSO)

147

What structural features do we look for in order to identify 'good' nucleophiles for the S_N2 reaction?

(A)

General form of "Bulky" Poor Nu	Examples of Poor Nu	Examples of Good Nu
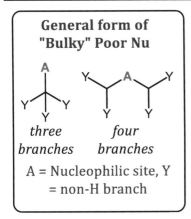 *three branches* / *four branches* A = Nucleophilic site, Y = non-H branch	F^-, H_2O, HOR 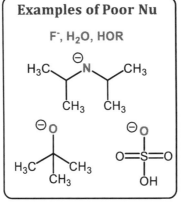	Cl^-, Br^-, I^-, HO^- 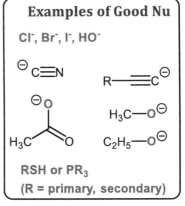 RSH or PR_3 (R = primary, secondary)

Notes

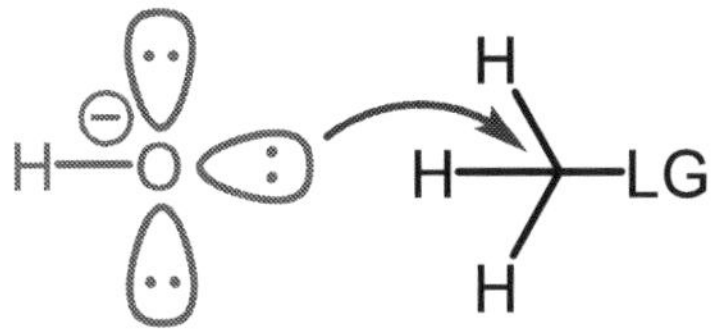

(A)

(B)

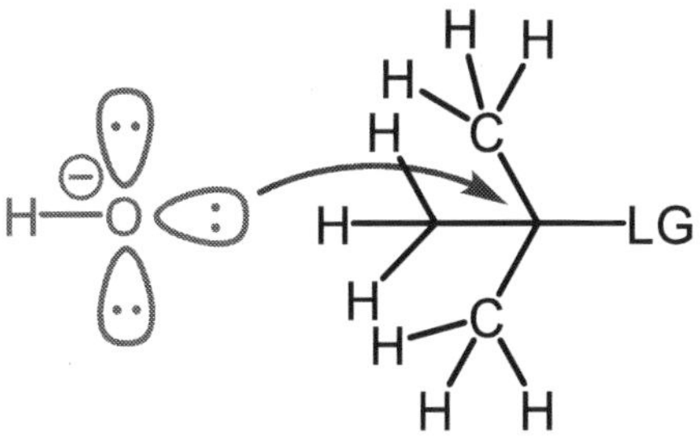

Similar to how steric hindrance slows bulky Nucleophiles

(C)   This observation about sterics allows us to predict S$_N$2 rates:

Tertiary halides do not work for S$_N$2 due to sterics!

Notes

A

Solvent weakens Nu strength

B

Solvent can stabilize anions
(we saw this for bases)

The influence on Nu strength influences the rate to a greater extent than does the stabilization of the anion, so:

C

Notes

Recall from **Lecture Topic II.1** that a single chiral product cannot be obtained from achiral starting materials for **any** step of a reaction sequence. Consider the reaction of a chiral alkyl halide by an S$_N$1 pathway:

(R)-isomer Br   Br (S)-isomer

C_2H_5⋯⋯⋯*⟋CH₃   H₃C⟍*⋯⋯⋯C_2H_5
      H   H

heterolysis

After heterolysis, Chirality is lost. We cannot even tell from which of the two isomers the cation was formed!

(A)

An Achiral Carbocation

Notes

This type of heterolysis is sometimes casually referred to as "leaving group leaves"

S$_N$1

no carbocation rearrangement

X⁻

ΔG

S$_N$1

(R-) Achiral (R-) (S-)

50:50 MIXTURE = racemic mixture

The carbocation formed by heterolysis has a trigonal planar geometry; it is achiral and symmetric. The nucleophile may attack from either face of the plane with equal probability:

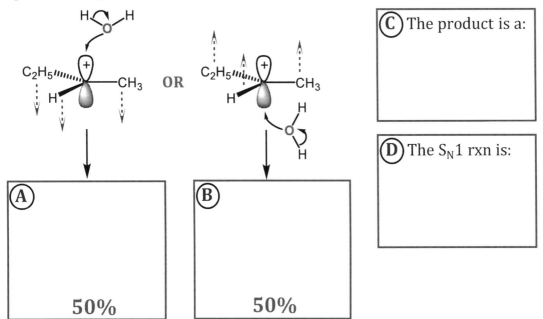

OR

(C) The product is a:

(D) The S$_N$1 rxn is:

(A)

50%

(B)

50%

Notes

The S$_N$2 reaction is concerted, so if the nucleophile substitutes at a stereogenic site, a single chiral compound will be produced:

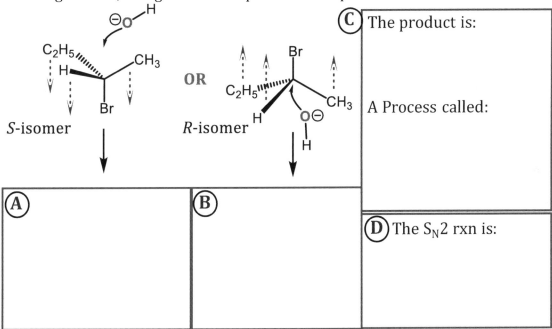

S-isomer   OR   R-isomer

(C) The product is:

A Process called:

(A)

(B)

(D) The S$_N$2 rxn is:

Notes JN2

Transition State

Walden Inversion

Br

NaCN

CN

R-

S-

Br

Et

Me

H

C≡N

[Br δ- ...... Me

Et — C ...... H

O δ-

C

N]

Et

Me

H

C

N

R always switches to S

wedge does not alway switch to hashed

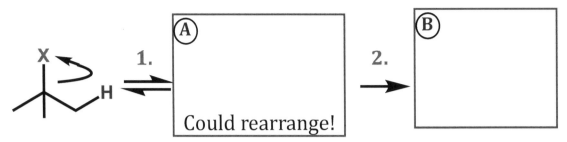

(A) Could rearrange!

1.

2.

(B)

This is the E1 reaction: Heterolysis then electrophilic elimination.
Heterolysis is rate-limiting, as in S_N1. The intermediate carbocation can also rearrange. In fact, many aspects of E1 are similar to S_N1:

Rate Law: **(C)**

Substrate: **(D)**

Leaving Group: **(E)**

Solvent: **(F)**

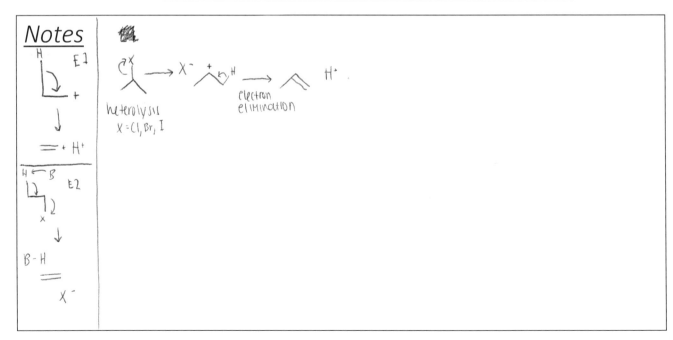

Notes

E1

+

$= + H^+$

E2

B-H

X^-

heterolysis
X = Cl, Br, I

electron
elimination

H^+

Once heterolysis occurs to generate the carbocation intermediate, there may be more than one possible electrophilic elimination to consider:

We know that stability is important in predicting product distribution. Alkene stabilities have been measured (more on how in **Lecture Topic III.2**) and found follow this trend (R = a hydrocarbon substituent):

LESS STABLE   MORE STABLE

Notes E1

$$C \overset{X}{\wedge} \rightarrow \overset{+}{\wedge} + X^-$$

slow

- More stable LG = faster
- More stable carbocation = faster
- H-bonding solvent = faster
  (polar protic)

E1

Major product
best
yield

MOST stable
not eclipsing
two C coming off

Zaitsav's Rule

Observation = "Zaitsev's Rule:

Explanation = Energy (represented by a reaction coordinate diagram)

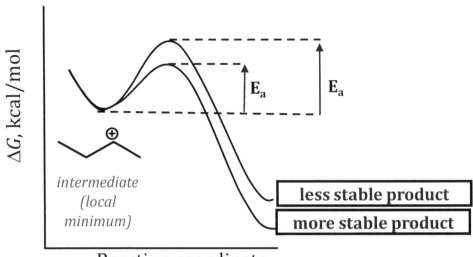

p

Notes

156

Lecture Topic II.6: The E1 Mechanism
Conformational Analysis Helps Determine Product Configuration

(A)

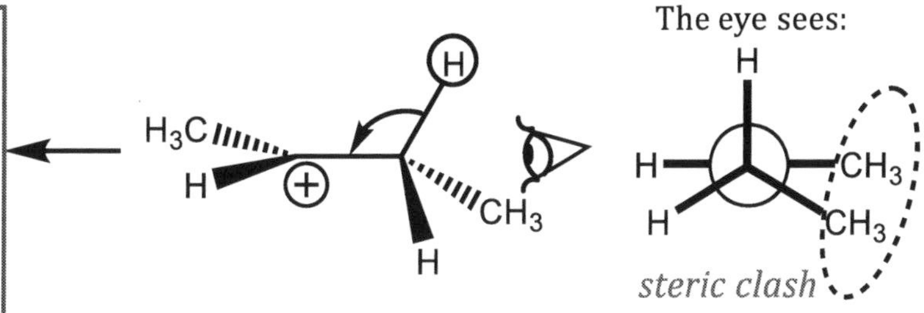
H_3C
H
H
CH_3
H
The eye sees:
H
H
CH_3
H
CH_3
steric clash

(B)

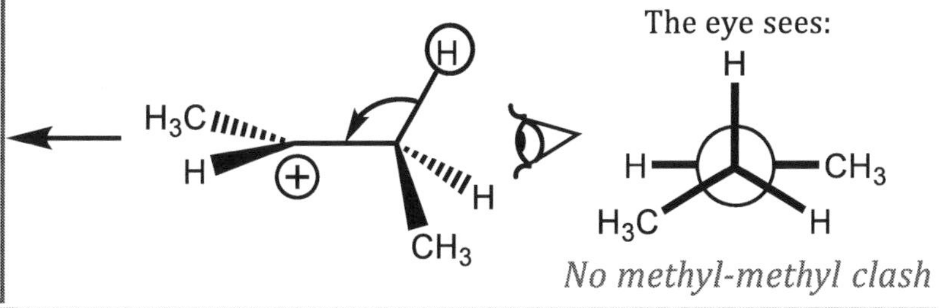
H_3C
H
H
H
CH_3
The eye sees:
H
H
CH_3
H_3C
H
No methyl-methyl clash

(C)

Notes

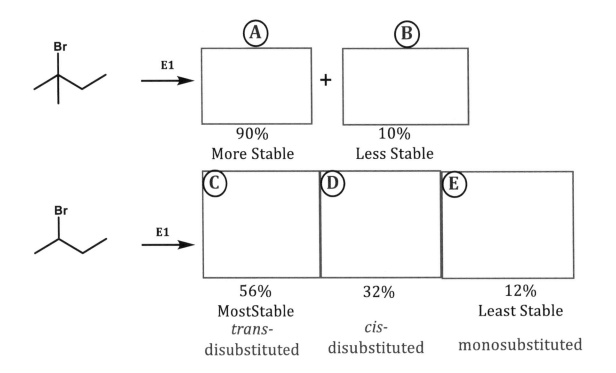

A 90% More Stable + B 10% Less Stable

C 56% MostStable *trans-* disubstituted

D 32% *cis-* disubstituted

E 12% Least Stable monosubstituted

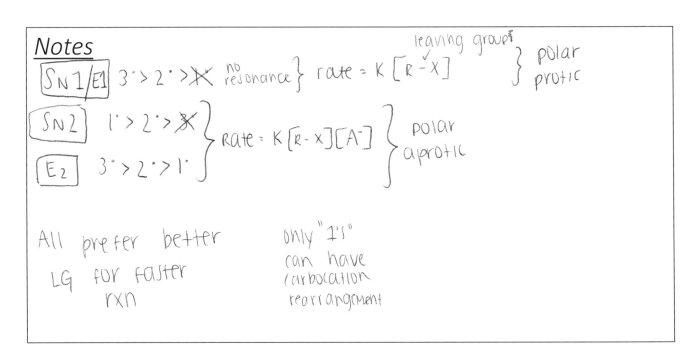

Notes

$\boxed{SN1/E1}$ 3° > 2° > 1̷° no resonance } rate = K $[R-X]$ leaving group } polar protic

$\boxed{SN2}$ 1° > 2° > 3̷° } Rate = K $[R-X][A^-]$ } polar aprotic

$\boxed{E_2}$ 3° > 2° > 1°

All prefer better
LG for faster
rxn

only "1's"
can have
carbocation
reorrangement

We learned the general form of the E2 reaction in **Lecture Topic I.8**.
We will now study this mechanistic step is more detail.

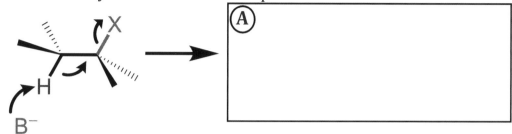

(A)

(B) Like the S_N2 reaction, the E2 reaction occurs in a single step. This
type of reaction is called a:

(C) That there is only one step means that base, substrate and leaving
group all influence rate. The rate law is:

A stronger base and better leaving group lead to faster rate.

Notes

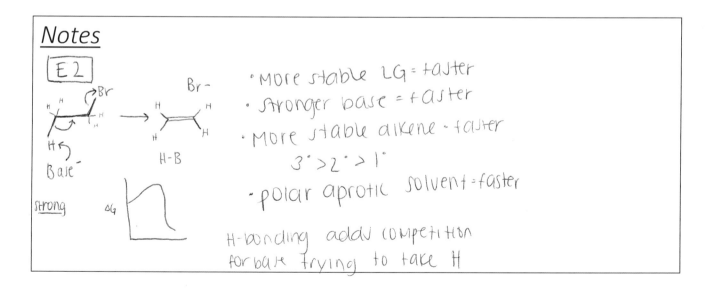

E2

H-B

Strong   ΔG

Base⁻

Br-

• More stable LG = faster
• Stronger base = faster
• More stable alkene = faster
     3° > 2° > 1°
• polar aprotic solvent = faster

H-bonding adds competition
for base trying to take H

(A)

H-bonding solvents weaken Bases

A strong base is necessary for a rapid E2 reaction of an alkyl halide. H-bonding solvents (polar protic solvents) weaken base strength. Therefore:

(B)

It is also observed that more substituted alkyl halides react faster:

(C)

How can we use our knowledge of reactions to explain this observation?

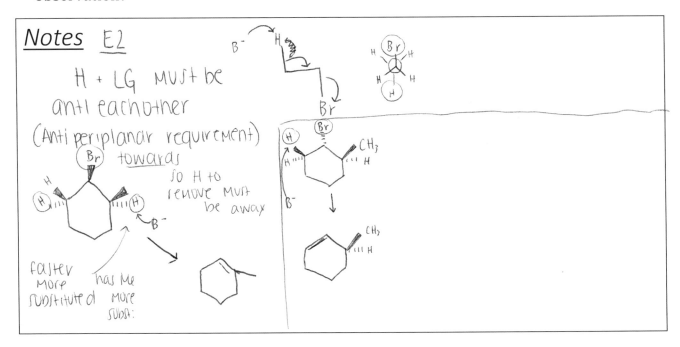

Notes E2

H + LG MUST be anti eachother

(Anti periplanar requirement)

Br towards
so H to remove MUST be away

faster More substituted

has Me More subst:

More substituted alkyl halides yield more substituted alkenes

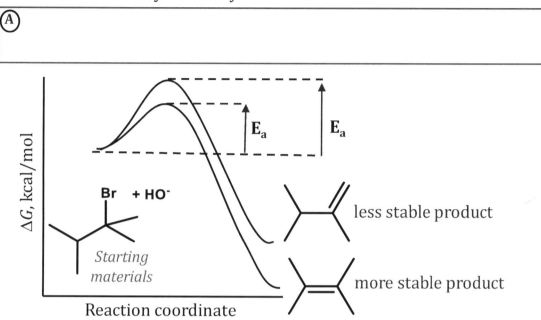

The E2 reactions generally follow "Zaitsev's Rule" like E1 reactions do.

In order for the E2 reaction to work, the H and X to be eliminated must be **antiperiplanar**.

"Antiperiplanar" means the two groups are in the *anti-* conformation and in the same plane.

This is what is known as a **stereoelectronic** effect:

(A)

Notes

The stereoelectronic requirements of the E2 reaction must be considered when we attempt to predict products of a reaction.

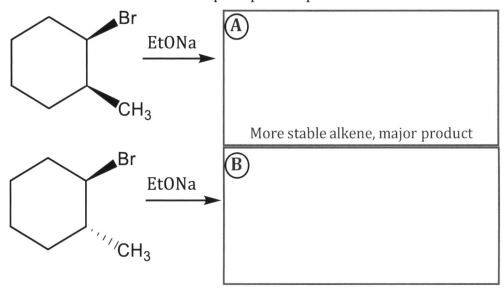

(A)

More stable alkene, major product

(B)

Less stable alkene, but no antiperiplanar H available for elimination to form more stable alkene. Note that the configuration about the chiral C is preserved because it was not involved in the reaction.

Notes

For reaction on a cyclohexane derivative, eliminated groups must be axial to be antiperiplanar. If the eliminated H and leaving group are not axial in the most stable conformation, a ring flip may be necessary (may need to heat to accomplish this):

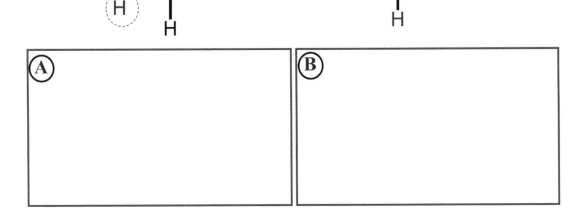

(A)

(B)

<u>Notes</u>

Example. The *cis-* isomer of 1-bromo-4-*t*-butylcyclohexane reacts by E2 reaction 500 times faster than does the *trans-* isomer. Why?

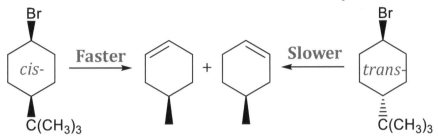

Start by drawing each reagent with Br (leaving group) in an axial position, where it must be for an E2 reaction to take place:

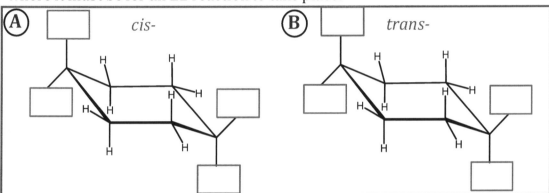

Notes

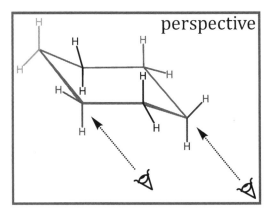

perspective

In the *cis-* conformation, when the leaving group is axial, the sterically encumbered *t*-butyl is equatorial. In the *trans-* conformation, both *t*-butyl and bromide can be equatorial. As a result, the *trans-* isomer reacts much more slowly (needs an energetically unfavorable ring flip to get Br axial to react!)

cis-

trans-

Notes

166

There are instances when only one H is present for elimination to form the most-substituted alkene. In these cases the antiperiplanar requirement may enforce formation of one alkene stereoisomer:

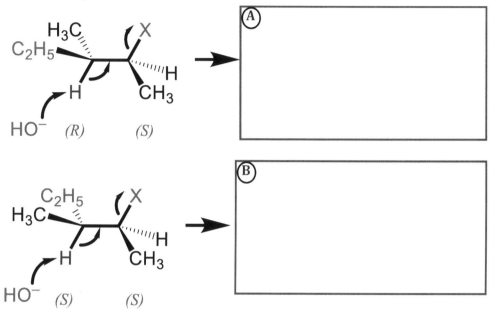

Notes

167

Steric hindrance to deprotonate a sterically-encumbered site increases as
the base becomes bulkier:

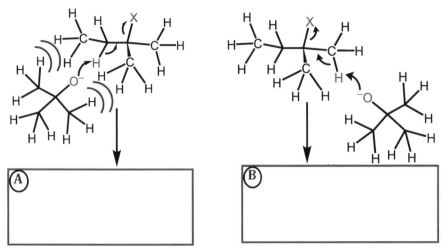

(A)

(B)

As a result:

(C)

Notes

The less-substituted product (non-Zaitsev) is sometimes called the

(A)

This terminology came from a clever version of the E2 reaction in which the leaving group is a bulky amine. This variation is called the:

(B)

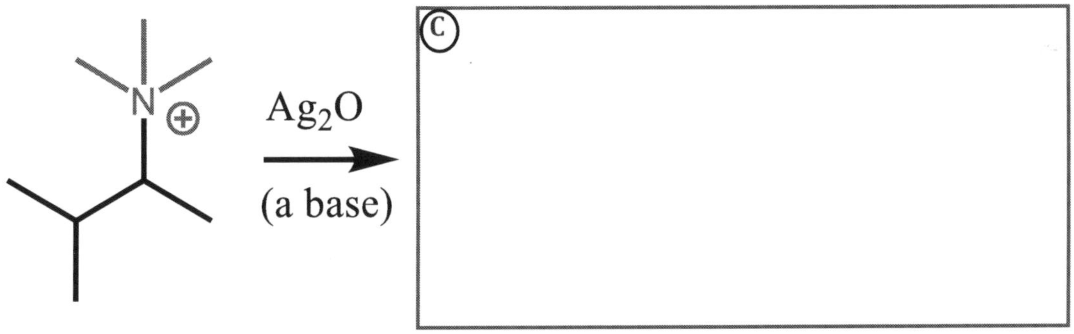

Ag_2O

$\xrightarrow{\hspace{2cm}}$

(a base)

(C)

Conformational analysis may help us visualize and explain why the Hofmann product is favored...

Notes

On the left is the conformation necessary to produce the Zaitsev Product. On the right is the conformation necessary to produce the Hofmann Product.

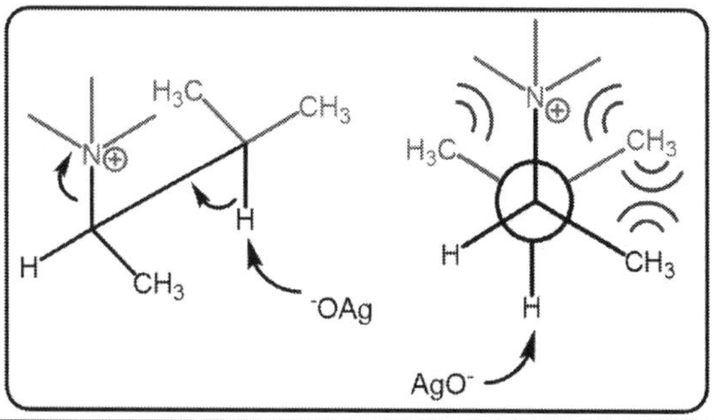

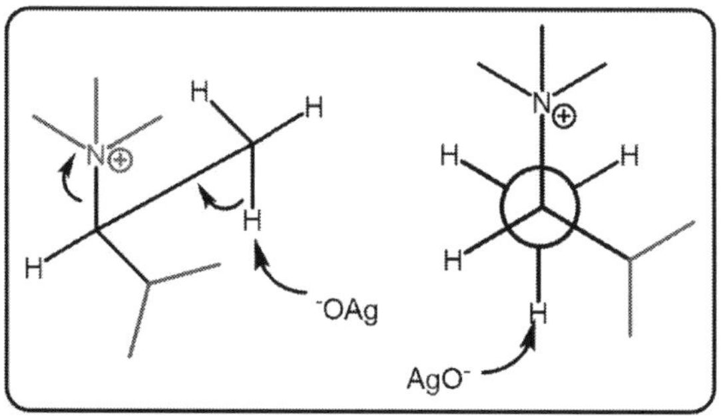

(A) Product:

Disfavored because:

(B) Product:

Favored because:

Notes

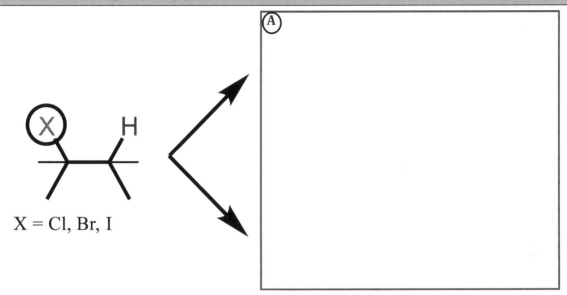

$X = Cl, Br, I$

In a given context: 1. Elimination or Substitution?
                        2. E1, S_N1, E2, or S_N2?

Notes

Bimolecular reaction (S_N2, E2) are favored by high concentration of good Nu or strong B

good Nu, weak B   (i.e., I⁻, Br⁻, HS⁻, NH_3): Ⓐ

good Nu, strong B (i.e., HO⁻, EtO⁻, H_2N^-): Ⓑ

poor Nu, strong B (i.e., ${}^tBuO^-$, bulky): Ⓒ

Substrate can also help determine E2 versus S_N2
    1° RX   no bulky base: Ⓓ

    BULKY base (i.e., ⁻O^tBu): Ⓔ
    2° RX   **S_N2 and E2**;
            the stronger/bulkier the base, the more **E2**
    3° RX   **E2 only**

Unimolecular reactions (S_N1, E1) are favored when neither a good nucleophile nor a strong base

Notes

Is there a Good Nu or Strong B?

NO   YES

1° R-X
no resonance   other R-X   Ⓒ
Ⓐ   Ⓑ   Strong B
                         Poor Nu   Strong B
                                                              Good Nu
                                          Ⓓ   Ⓔ
                                        1° R-X   2°/3° R-X

                         Good Nu
                         Weak B

              1° or 2° R-X   3° R-X

                    Ⓕ   Ⓖ

Notes

	Reagent			
Substrate	Poor Nu/Weak Base	Good Nu/Weak B	Good Nu/Strong B	Poor Nu/Strong B
CH$_3$–X				
1° R–X				
2° R–X				
3° R–X				

Notes

Example. Determine whether each reaction will proceed predominantly via S_N1, S_N2, E1, E2, or some combination thereof, and show the product(s)

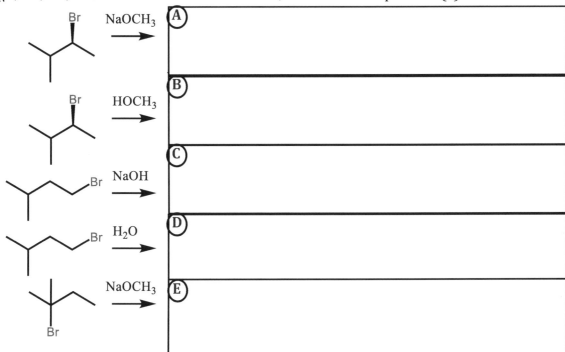

Notes

Example. Predict whether each proceeds via S_N1, S_N2, E1, or E2, and draw the major product (show stereochemistry where applicable).

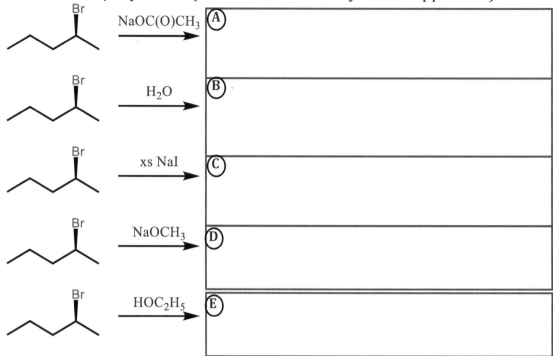

Br
⟶ NaOC(O)CH₃ (A)

Br
⟶ H₂O (B)

Br
⟶ xs NaI (C)

Br
⟶ NaOCH₃ (D)

Br
⟶ HOC₂H₅ (E)

Notes

So far we have only explored alkyl halides as substrates for S_N1, S_N2, E1 or E2 reactions because alkyl halides with Cl, Br or I substituents have the good leaving groups required. If we propose using an alcohol in these reactions:

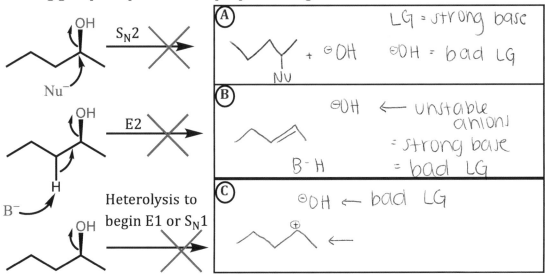

The hydroxide anion is a strong base (unstable anion) and is a bad leaving group. It must be **activated** prior to reaction by these routes.

<u>*Notes*</u>

177

One way to convert OH into a good leaving group is to protonate it with a strong acid. This leads to a water leaving group. This allows **a tertiary or secondary alcohol to undergo an S_N1 reaction**:

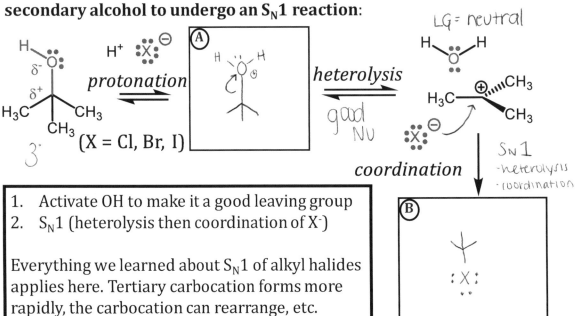

1. Activate OH to make it a good leaving group
2. S_N1 (heterolysis then coordination of X⁻)

Everything we learned about S_N1 of alkyl halides applies here. Tertiary carbocation forms more rapidly, the carbocation can rearrange, etc.

<u>Notes</u>

An activated **methyl or 1° alcohol will undergo S$_N$2 reaction** with the
halide, which is a good nucleophile:

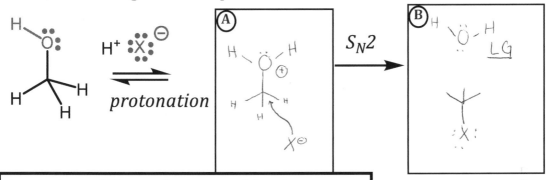

1. Activate OH to make it a good leaving group
2. S$_N$2 (concerted)

Everything we learned about S$_N$2 of alkyl halides
applies here. Walden inversion occurs, less
sterically-encumbered substrates react faster,
etc.

Notes

179

If a 2° or 3° alcohol is activated with an acid having a non-nucleophilic counteranion (i.e., H_2SO_4 or H_3PO_4), an E1 Reaction will occur. Net reaction is loss of water from the alcohol, this particular type of E1 reaction is also called **dehydration**.

1. Activate OH to make it a good leaving group
2. E1 (heterolysis then electrophilic elimination)

Everything we learned about E1 of alkyl halides applies here. Tertiary carbocation forms more rapidly, the carbocation can rearrange, etc.
Note: cannot do E2 (needs strong **base**) of an alcohol with strong acid!

Notes   E1   E2   Alcohol → good LG
              needs ←———→ strong acid
              strong incompatible
              base

Another way to activate an OH group is by reaction with PX_3 (X = Cl or Br):

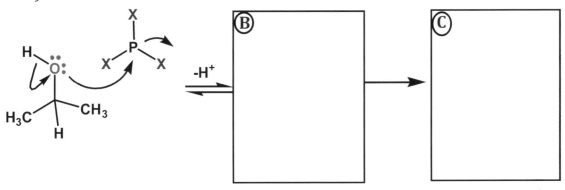

1. Activate leaving group
2. S_N2 reaction – all we have learned about S_N2 applies here; it will not work on a tertiary alcohol, for example.

Note: 1 mol PX_3 can produce 3 mol RX + H_3PO_3

Notes

A third way to activate an OH group is by reaction with thionyl chloride:

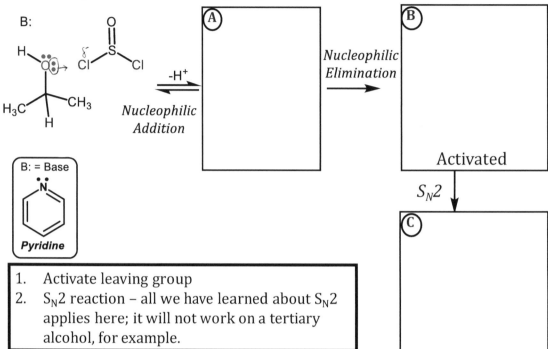

B: = Base

Pyridine

1. Activate leaving group
2. S_N2 reaction – all we have learned about S_N2 applies here; it will not work on a tertiary alcohol, for example.

Notes

182

Alcohols can also be converted into sulfonate esters. This is not a substitution or elimination reaction, but it is a good way to change the OH into a good leaving group:

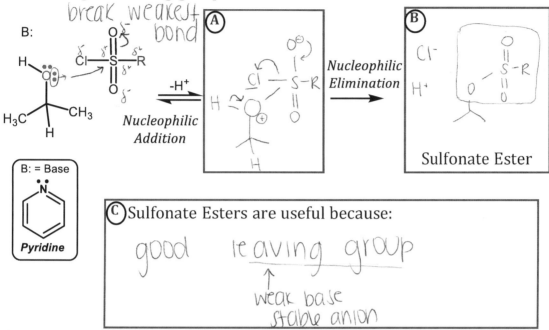

Nucleophilic Addition · *Nucleophilic Elimination*

(A) · **(B)** Sulfonate Ester

B: = Base

Pyridine

(C) Sulfonate Esters are useful because:

good leaving group
           ↑
      weak base
      stable anion

Notes

The sulfonate is a good leaving group because of resonance stabilization:

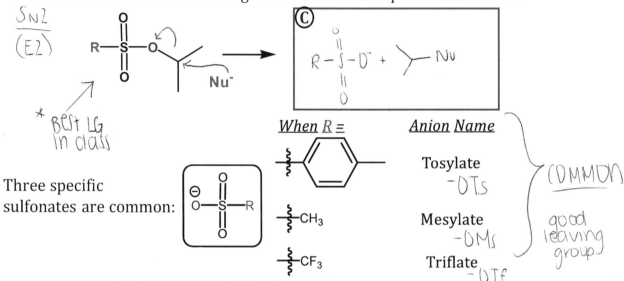

A sulfonate ester is ideal starting material for nucleophilic substitution:

	When R ≡	Anion Name	
	aromatic ring (para-substituted)	Tosylate $-OTs$	COMMON
Three specific sulfonates are common:	CH_3	Mesylate $-OMs$	good leaving group
	CF_3	Triflate $-OTf$	

Notes

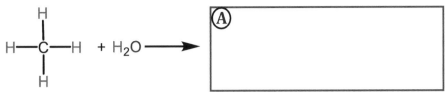

When methane burns in the presence to form carbon dioxide, it is said to undergo "oxidation". The opposite of oxidation is "reduction"

In general, the more C-H bonds that are replaced by C-O (or C to other more electronegative atom) bonds in an alkane, the more oxidized the carbon atom becomes:

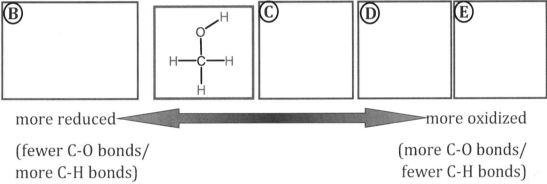

more reduced ⟵⟶ more oxidized

(fewer C-O bonds/
more C-H bonds)

(more C-O bonds/
fewer C-H bonds)

Notes

Lecture Topic II.13: Oxidation of Alcohols
Chromium Reagents are Commonly used to Oxidize Alcohols

Oxidation of alcohols is a useful way to make carboxylic acids, aldehydes, and ketones. Strong oxidizing agents like H^+/CrO_4^{2-}, H^+/Cr_2O_7, CrO_3/H_2SO_4 (Jones Oxidation) replace all C-H bonds of an alcohol C with C–O bonds. PCC is weaker and can only replace one C–H with a C–O bond:

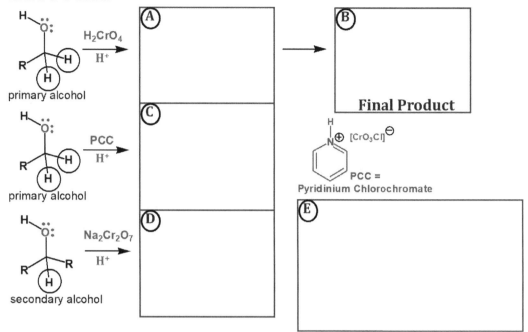

Final Product

PCC = Pyridinium Chlorochromate

Notes

186

Like alcohols, ethers do not have a good leaving group for substitution reactions. However, the O atom of an ether can be protonated by HX (X = Cl, Br, I) to create a good leaving group. An S_N1 or S_N2 reaction follows:

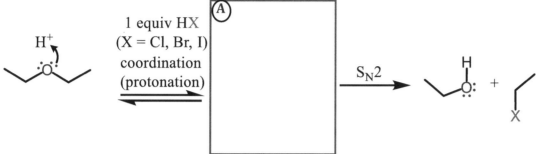

In this example, the ether is symmetric, so it does not matter which side we choose to attack with the nucleophile.

If the carbon to be attacked is methyl or primary:

(B)

Because:

Notes

If the carbon to be attacked by the nucleophile is 2° or 3°:

Ⓐ

This is the case even though a good nucleophile (Cl-, Br- or I-) is present, so this **is a difference from alkyl halides**.

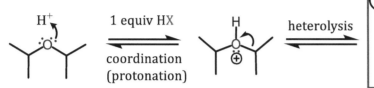

Ⓑ

coordination

Ⓒ

1. Activate OR to make it a good leaving group
2. S_N1 (heterolysis then coordination of X-)

Everything we learned about S_N1 of alkyl halides applies here. Tertiary carbocation forms more rapidly, the carbocation can rearrange, etc.

Notes

The ether may not be symmetrical. In these cases:

Ⓐ

If both sides of the ether are capable of S_N1, 3° reacts faster than 2°, as for any other S_N1 reaction. So:

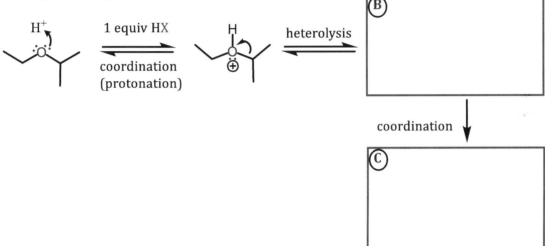

Ⓑ

coordination

Ⓒ

Notes

An epoxides is a specific type of ether consisting of a 3-membered ring having an oxygen atom in the ring:

Ⓐ

Epoxides are much more reactive than most other ethers because:

Ⓑ

Nucleophiles can thus attack one of the electrophilic carbon atoms, alleviating the ring strain:

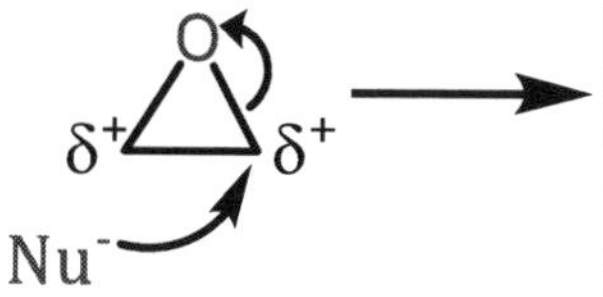

Ⓒ

δ^+ δ^+

Nu^-

Notes

Under basic (or simply non-acidic) conditions a typical S_N2 reaction occurs, which requires a good nucleophile:

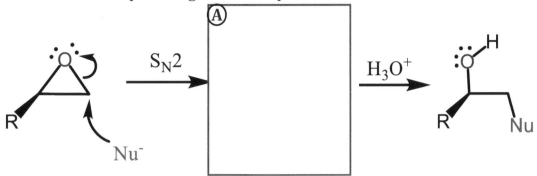

(A)

(B) Like other S_N2 reactions on neutral substrates, the nucleophile preferentially attacks:

Note that after ring-opening, the oxygen:

Notes

Under acidic conditions, the epoxide oxygen is protonated just as in acid cleavage of other ethers:

H^+

coordination (protonation)

S_N2

(A)

(B)

The less substituted side is attacked unless there is a tertiary site. A tertiary C next to an O with formal charge of +1 has a lot of positive charge, and will be attacked preferentially:

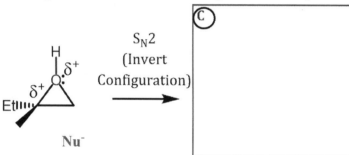

S_N2
(Invert Configuration)

(C)

Nu⁻

Under acidic conditions, the nucleophile will attack the tertiary C if there is one. Otherwise, the less-hindered side is attacked, just as under basic conditions.

Notes

Example. Predict the major product of each reaction, showing stereochemistry where applicable.

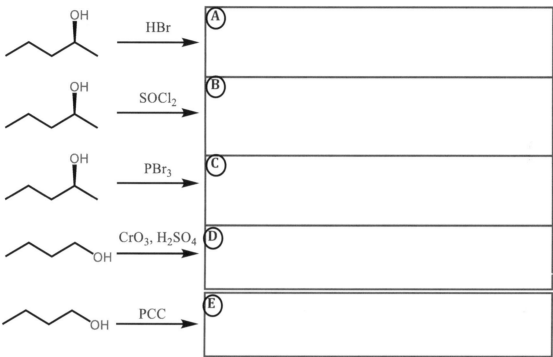

Notes

Example. Predict the major product of each reaction, showing stereochemistry where applicable.

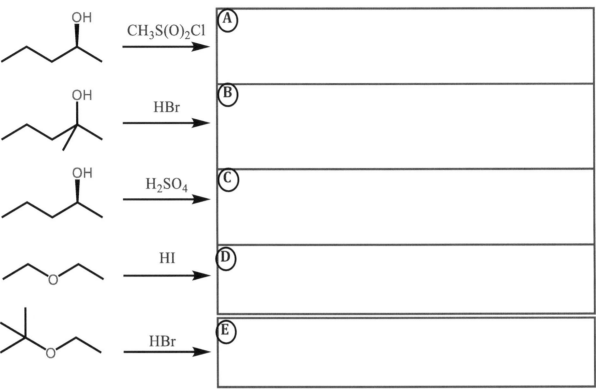

(A)

(B)

(C)

(D)

(E)

Notes

194

Example. Predict the major product of each reaction, showing stereochemistry where applicable.

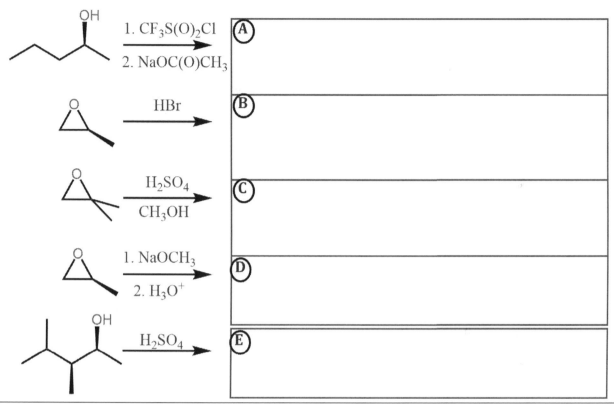

Notes

Nomenclature of alkenes is related to that for alkanes, with modifications:

1. always designate the longest chain having

(A) [   ] as the parent chain.

2. Number the parent chain such that the double bond

(B) [   ]

4. change the 'ane' ending of the name you would use if it were an alkane

(C) [   ]

5. Tell where the double bond starts:

(D) [   ]

Notes

196

Lecture Topic III.1: Nomenclature of Alkenes
Naming Simple Alkenes

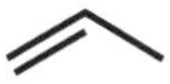
propene

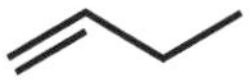
1-butene

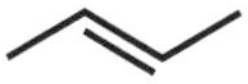
2-butene

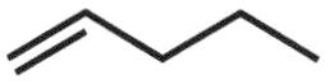
1-pentene

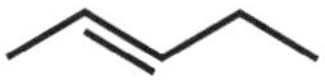
2-pentene

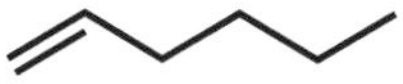
1-hexene

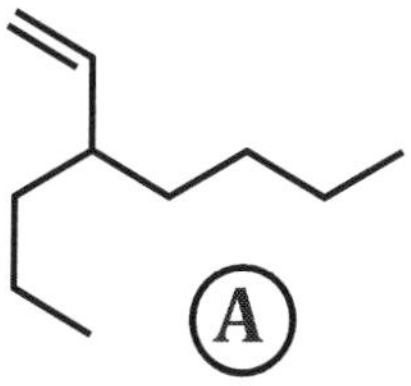
(A)

Notes

6. If there is more than one double bond, use a "-diene", "-triene", etc. at the end of the name in place of the "ene", with multiple numbers indicating where the double bonds are:

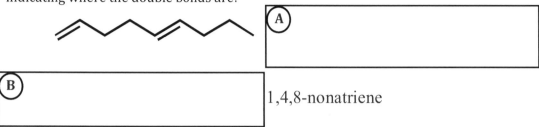

A _____

B _____

1,4,8-nonatriene

7. If an alcohol is present, it has higher priority than the, and the molecule has an "-ol" ending (with a number to tell you where the OH is!) after the "ene" suffix (change "ene" to "en"), and the **alcohol is given the lowest number**:

3-penten-2-ol

C _____

4-penten-1-ol

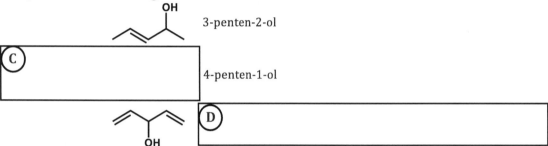

D _____

Notes

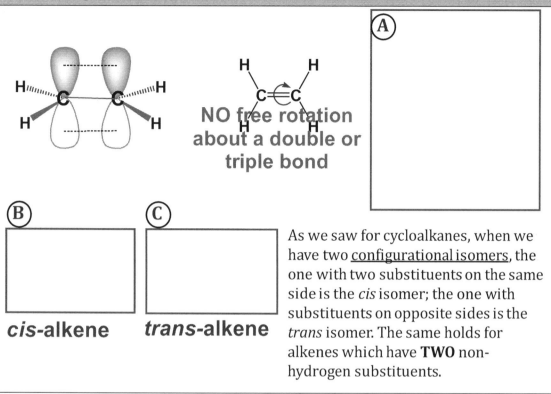

NO free rotation about a double or triple bond

Ⓐ

Ⓑ

cis-alkene

Ⓒ

trans-alkene

As we saw for cycloalkanes, when we have two <u>configurational isomers</u>, the one with two substituents on the same side is the *cis* isomer; the one with substituents on opposite sides is the *trans* isomer. The same holds for alkenes which have **TWO** non-hydrogen substituents.

Notes

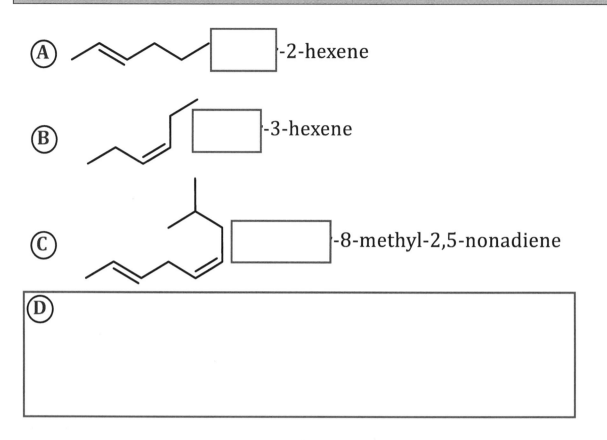

Ⓐ [ ]-2-hexene

Ⓑ [ ]-3-hexene

Ⓒ [ ]-8-methyl-2,5-nonadiene

Ⓓ

<u>Notes</u>

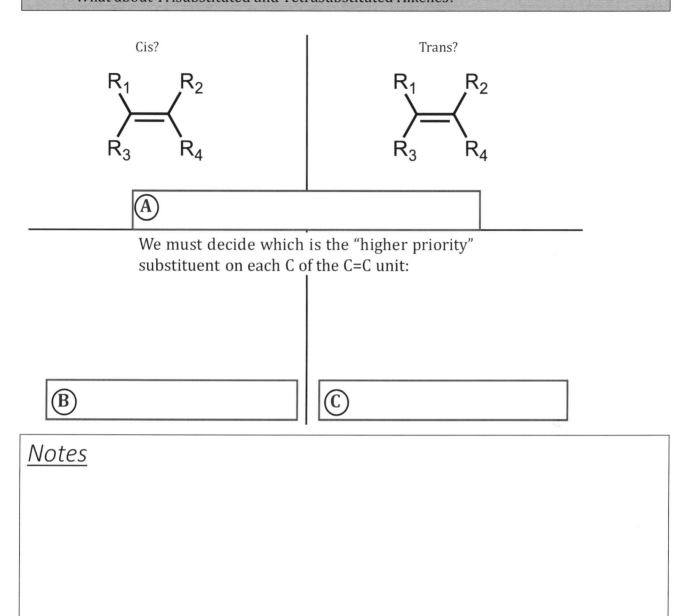

Cis?

Trans?

(A)

We must decide which is the "higher priority"
substituent on each C of the C=C unit:

(B)

(C)

Notes

For tri- or tetra-substituted alkenes we use *E*- (from German 'entgegen', opposite) or *Z*- (from German 'zusammen', together) notation. We prioritize units using CIP conventions (See **Topic I.20**)

If the two **highest priority groups** (are

on same side, then (A)

opposite sides, then (B)

(C)

(D)

Z-isomer   E-isomer

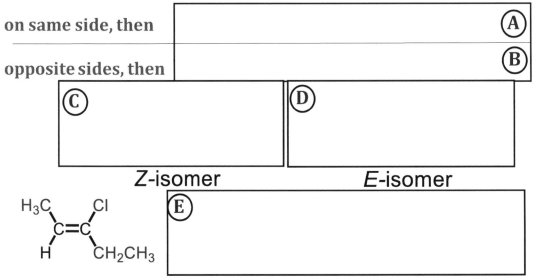

(E)

Notes

Example. Designate each double bond as *E-* or *Z-*.

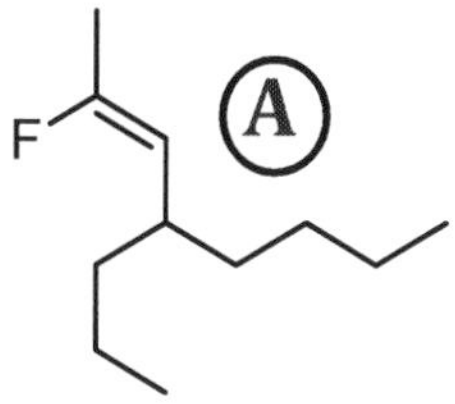

(A)

(B)

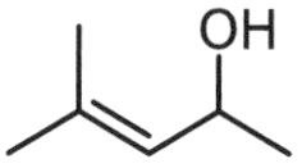

(C)

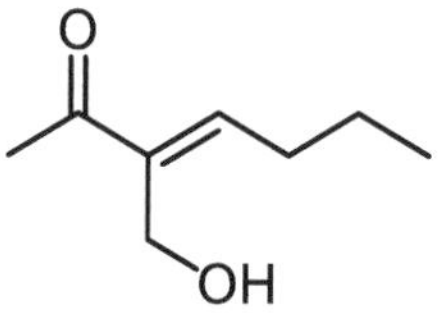

(D)

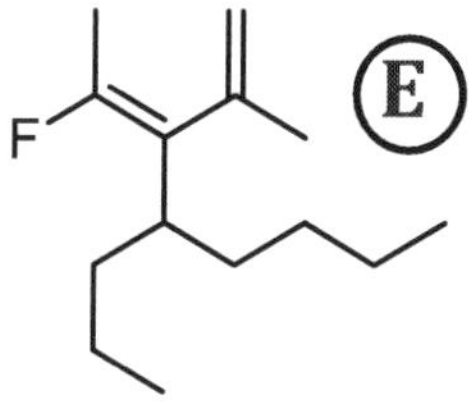

(E)

Notes

Alkanes: C_nH_{2n+2} **saturated** hydrocarbons

Alkenes: C_nH_{2n} **unsaturated** hydrocarbons (put a double bond in an alkane)
(olefins)

Each removal of two hydrogens from a saturated hydrocarbon (alkane) is one degree of unsaturation (can add one H_2 molecule to it)

A **degree of unsaturation** can be:

A general formula to determine the degree of unsaturation of a molecule from its formula ($C_cH_hN_nO_oX_x$, where X = F, Cl, Br or I) is:

*Note that oxygen's presence does not impact the degree of unsaturation

Notes

Alkenes can be prepared by elimination reactions. Alkenes can also undergo

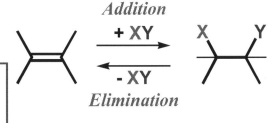

Addition

+ XY

- XY

Elimination

(A)

addition rxns

A stereochemical/mechanistic issue to be addressed is whether a given addition reaction occurs with the resultant substituents adding *syn-* or *anti-* to one another:

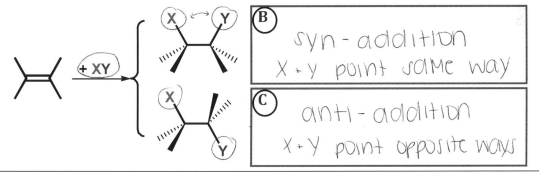

(B)

syn - addition
X + y point same way

(C)

anti - addition
X + y point opposite ways

Notes

We have observed the following trend in alkene stability:

1. More substituted = More stable

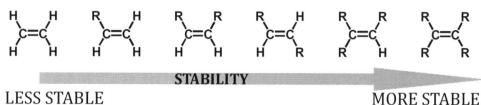

STABILITY

LESS STABLE   MORE STABLE

These stabilities are determined by doing a **hydrogenation** of the alkene and measuring the heat given off by the process. Hydrogenation (**addition of two H atoms to the pi bond**) is accomplished by reacting with $H_2(g)$ and a Pd or Pt catalyst:

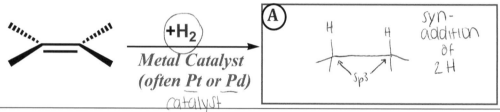

Metal Catalyst
(often Pt or Pd)
catalyst

Notes

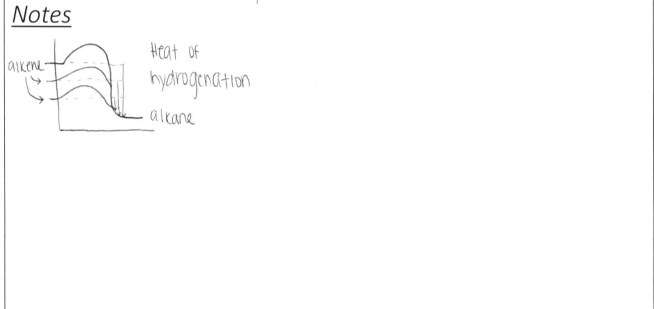

General Reaction:

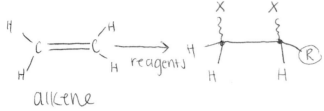

good
summary

allcene

Considerations:

- Which things add to the C=C?

  depends on reagents

- If the two sides are different, which adds to which C?

  Markovinikov's Rule : more electronegative
  atom binds more substituted Carbon

- Is there a carbocation that could rearrange (like for E1 and S$_N$1)?

  Yes, if strong acid & no peroxides

Notes

More Complex Considerations:

- Do the two things I add end up *anti-* or *syn-* to each other?

    learn Mechanisms
        ↳ recognize trends

- What if there are stereocenters or I make stereocenters?

    all principles from lesson II.1 apply

- What are the mechanisms?

    lessons III.4 - .9

Notes

What Adds?

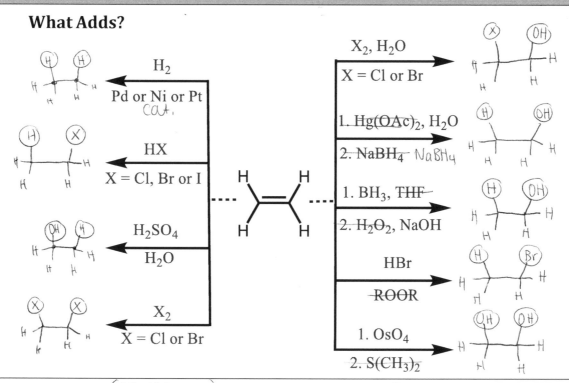

Notes

(HCl, HBr, HI)
        (or H₂)

Strong Acids (HX or H_2SO_4): add H

[(ROH)]
Water or NaOH or OsO_4: add $-OH$
                          [RO-]

X_2: X—| X = Cl, Br, I

HX: X—|

BH₃ or NaBH₄: |—H

all else is extraneous

Which side gets the more electronegative atom bound to it?

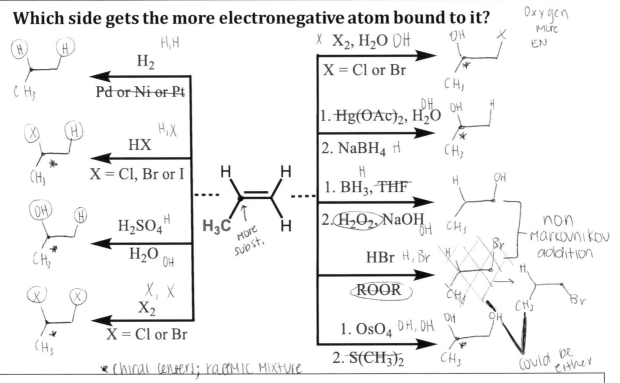

Oxygen
More
EN

* chiral centers; racemic mixture

Notes

More E.N. adds to more subst: Markovnikov's Rule
                  almost everything

More E.N adds to less subst:
           ones w/ peroxides

Peroxides such as ROOR or H_2O_2 (HOOH, hydrogen peroxide):

$\xrightarrow[\substack{peroxides \\ (ROOR)}]{HBr}$ $\xrightarrow[\substack{2. H_2O_2, NaOH, \\ H_2O}]{1. BH_3}$

Achiral $\xrightarrow{\times}$ one chiral product
          $\searrow$ racemic mix
             (2 enantiomers)

Is there a carbocation that can rearrange?

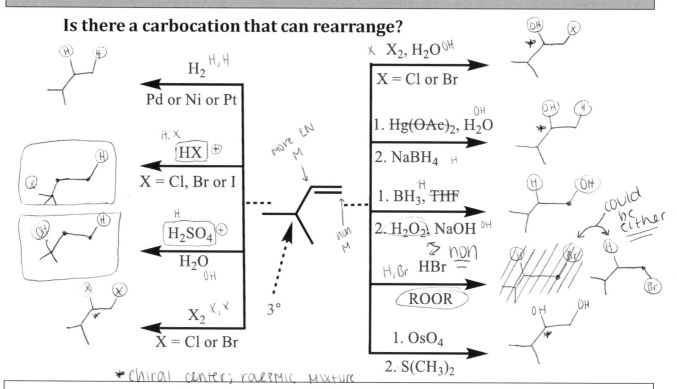

H_2 H, H
Pd or Ni or Pt

H, X
$\boxed{HX}$ ⊕
X = Cl, Br or I

H
$\boxed{H_2SO_4}$ ⊕
H_2O OH

X_2 X, X
X = Cl or Br

3°

more EN
M

non
M

X X_2, H_2O OH
X = Cl or Br

1. Hg(OAc)$_2$, H_2O OH
2. NaBH$_4$ H

1. BH$_3$, ~~THF~~ H
2. H_2O_2, NaOH OH
⇒ non

H, Br HBr — non
$\boxed{ROOR}$

1. OsO$_4$
2. S(CH$_3$)$_2$

could be either

*chiral center; racemic mixture

Notes

Strong acids without added peroxides:

HX or H$_2$SO$_4$
(sulfuric)

then make carbocation
on more substituted
C=C

2°

1°

HCl

2°
3°
3°

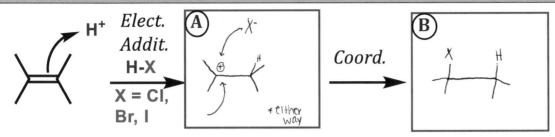

A * either way

B

Elect. Addit. H-X X = Cl, Br, I

Coord.

The mechanism is the reverse of **C** E1

The rate limiting step is

D step 1, Make C⁺ (carbocation) least stable products

The carbocation can: **E** rearrange

Addition is:

F hydrohalogenation

Notes

NaOH, H₂O, OsO₄ : OH

HOR : OR

H₂, Hx, H₂SO₄, BH (BH₃, NaBH₄) : H

X₂, HX : X

All else extraneous

Peroxide : H₂O₂, ROOR (non-Markovnikov's rule)

can only rearrange
    if strong acid : HX, H₂SO₄

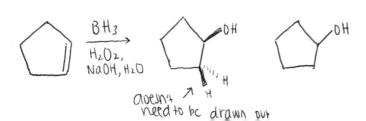

BH₃
H₂O₂,
NaOH, H₂O

doesn't need to be drawn out

substituents that are not Hydrogen

212

If the two pi-bonded carbon atoms are differently-substituted, there will be two choices for carbocation formation upon electrophilic addition:

A 3°

Major product

B 1°

The **major product** is that derived from the more stable carbocation, in this case the tertiary cation.

Notes

Strong acid or Hg(OAc)₂ : Mix of syn + Anti
X₂ : Anti
everything else: syn addition

213

* What adds? Where add? Rearrange? How pointing? *
chirality?

OBSERVATION= Markovnikov's rule:

Ⓐ

EXPLANATION=

Ⓑ

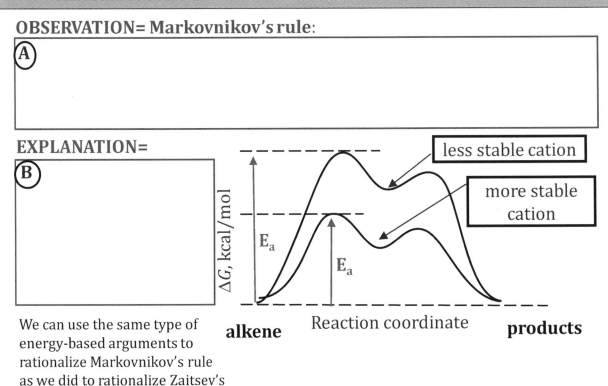

ΔG, kcal/mol

E_a

E_a

less stable cation

more stable cation

alkene   Reaction coordinate   **products**

We can use the same type of energy-based arguments to rationalize Markovnikov's rule as we did to rationalize Zaitsev's rule.

Notes

Remember that any time a carbocation is formed in the course of a reaction, you will need to assess whether it rearranges.

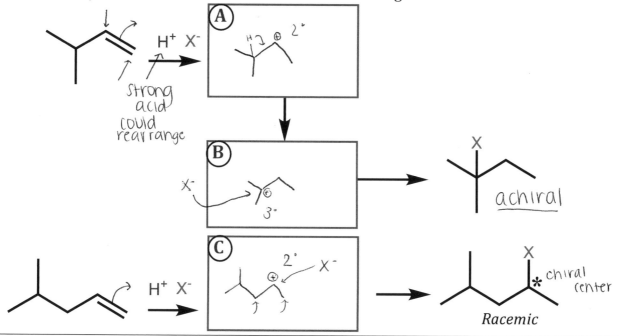

achiral

chiral center

Racemic

Notes

Addition of HX to an alkene is the reverse of E1 on an alkyl halide. We can also do a |hydration reaction| (addition of water to an alkene), which is the reverse of the dehydration (E1) of alcohols:

Ⓐ hydration rxn

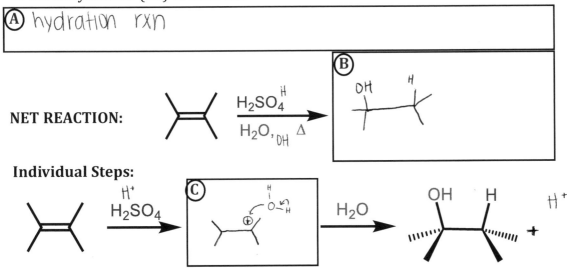

NET REACTION: Ⓑ

Individual Steps: Ⓒ

This reaction gives the Markovnikov product and has 50:50 syn-anti addition. The carbocation can rearrange just as for hydrohalogenation.

Notes

Recap

↓ SN2

racemic

When a halogen (Cl_2 or Br_2) comes in contact with an alkene, it sets off a series of events:

1. C=C pi electrons repel 'soft' electron cloud of halogen

2. This causes an induced dipole in the halogen:

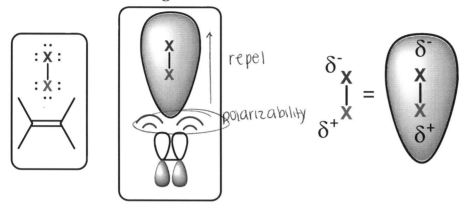

The partially positive end of the induced dipole now has an attraction for the nucleophilic alkene pi bond electrons ...

Notes

217

3. The polarized halogen begins an electrophilic addition to the alkene, losing $X^{:-}$

doesn't actually happen

4. As the positive charge begins to form on the carbon, a halogen lone pair is naturally attracted to it:

So that the final arrow pushing to give the resultant **halonium intermediate** and final S_N2 reaction is:

3 arrows

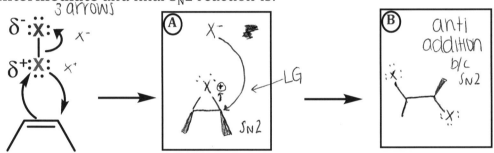

Ⓐ S_N2 Ⓑ anti addition b/c S_N2

S_N2 inverts
Walden Inversion

Notes

The formation of the halonium intermediate (chloronium if X = Cl, bromonium if X = Br) is concerted, so the relative distribution of substituents in the alkene is maintained. Keep in mind the stereochemistry!

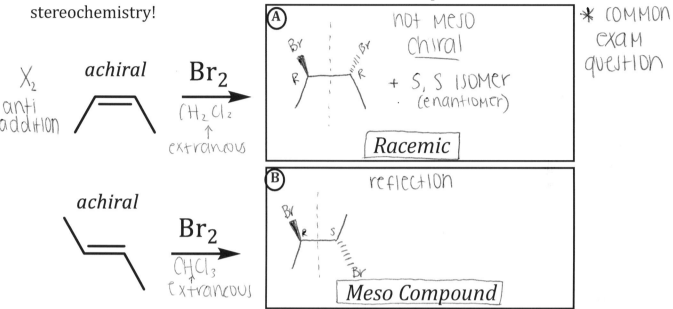

X_2
anti
addition

achiral

Br_2
CH_2Cl_2
↑
extraneous

(A) not meso
chiral
+ S, S isomer
(enantiomer)

Racemic

* common
exam
question

achiral

Br_2
$CHCl_3$
↑
extraneous

(B) reflection

Meso Compound

Notes

If an excess of water is present when the halonium intermediate forms, then the H_2O will serve as a nucleophile. A species in which an OH and Br units sit on adjacent carbon atoms is called a **Halohydrin**.

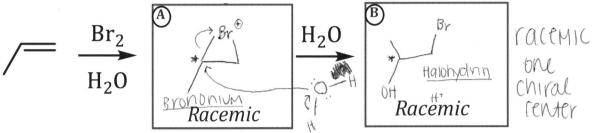

Note that since the water attacks the more substituted side, this is a **Markovnikov product**. The water attacks from the backside of the leaving group Br, so the OH and the Br end up **added *anti*** to one another:

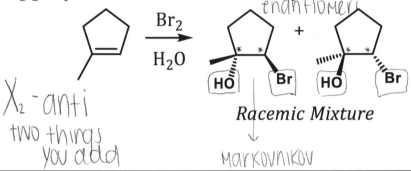

Notes

Alkenes react with $Hg(OAc)_2$ (mercuric acetate, $^-OAc = {^-OC(O)CH_3}$) to form a mercurinium intermediate:

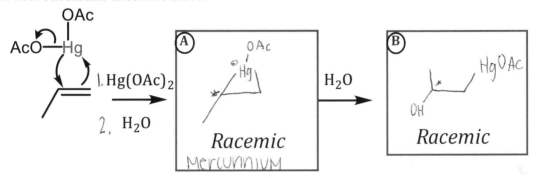

A *Racemic*
Mercurinium

B *Racemic*

You should recognize that the arrow-pushing to accomplish formation of the mercurinium intermediate in Box A is the same as for forming the halonium ions. Also, in the presence of water, the ring is opened by backside nucleophilic attack at the more substituted carbon in an S_N2 fashion.

Notes

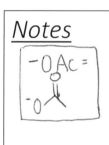

not concerted

The reaction of an alkene with $Hg(OAc)_2$ in the presence of water is called **oxymercuration**. One very useful second step is to replace the mercury with a hydrogen, so that the final species is an alcohol.

first
$Hg(OAc)_2$
H_2O

(A) OH ,,,HgOAc
anti - SN2

second
$NaBH_4$

(B) OH H ,,,H
MIX of syn ≠ anti

The net result is a **Markovnikov product.** The reduction step has a complex mechanism that is **not specific for *syn-* or *anti-* addition**. The Oxymercuration-reduction sequence is usually written on one arrow as:

1. $Hg(OAc)_2$, H_2O

2. $NaBH_4$

(C) OH H + its enantiomer
CH$_3$
Racemic Mixture

triangle, OH more substituted, H replaces mercury

Notes

epoxidation - concerted

222

Epoxidation is another **concerted** reaction that leads to the formation of a three-membered ring from an alkene. This reaction uses a **peroxyacid** (RC(O)OOR) as the reagent. A common peroxyacid used is mCPBA.

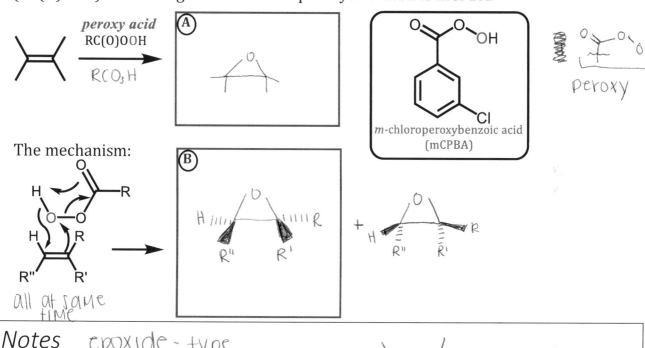

peroxy acid
RC(O)OOH

RCO₃H

Ⓐ

m-chloroperoxybenzoic acid
(mCPBA)

peroxy

The mechanism:

Ⓑ

all at same
time

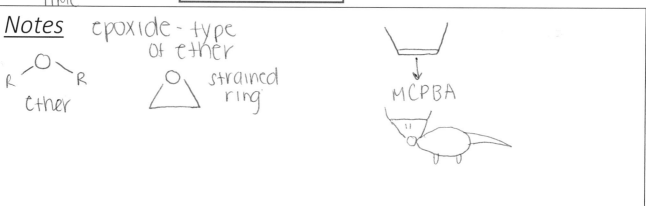

Notes   epoxide - type
              of ether

R—O—R
ether

△ strained
   ring

MCPBA

Epoxidation of several alkenes illustrates possible stereochemical outcomes:

all same type reagent
↓

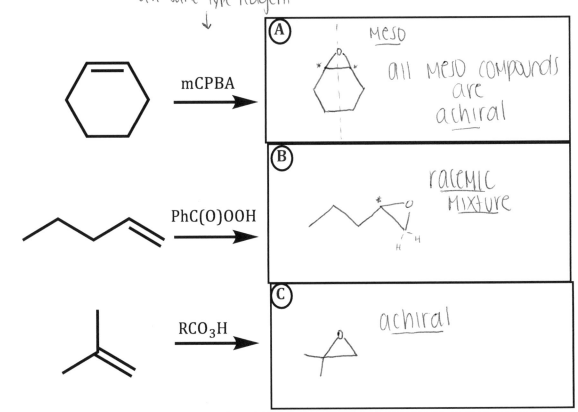

A MESO

all MESO compounds
are
achiral

mCPBA

PhC(O)OOH

B racemic
Mixture

RCO₃H

C achiral

Notes

Epoxidation of several alkenes illustrates possible stereochemical outcomes:

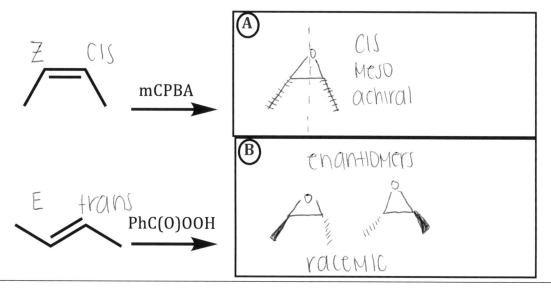

Notes

Like a carbene, a **borane** (BH_3, RBH_2 or R_2BH) has an empty p orbital, allowing it to accept a pair of electrons from an alkene. Unlike a carbene, borane does not have a lone pair, so it donates a bonding pair from its B–H bond, leading to **hydroboration** of the alkene:

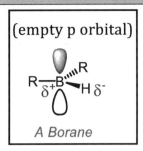

(empty p orbital)

A Borane

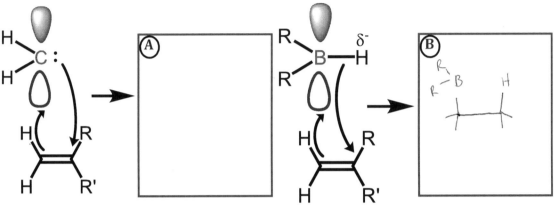

Ⓐ

Ⓑ

Notes

The **hydroboration step** is concerted and it leads to a **Markovnikov product** (H is more electronegative than B, so it ends up on the more substituted side). Because both B and H add at the same time, this is also a *syn*-**addition** step.

We can understand why H adds to the more substituted side if we examine the transition state and compare it to what we know about halonium formation (**Lecture Topic III.6**)

The more substituted C of the C=C bond better stabilizes positive charge, so the negative charge is attracted to that site

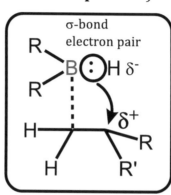

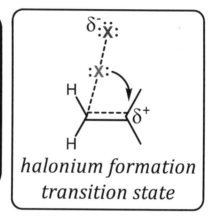

halonium formation transition state

Notes

227

The only application of hydroboration in this course is as part of a two-step process called **hydroboration-oxidation.** In this process the hydroboration is followed by an oxidation step in which the borane unit on the carbon is replaced with an OH without changing stereochemistry of attachment:

1. BH_3/THF

2. OH^-, H_2O_2, H_2O

replace B w/OH

(A) OH H   syn addition
               of OH + H
            non
            Markounikov

You may see "B_2H_6" or "R_2BH" (such as disiamylborane) in place of "BH_3/THF"; these are alternative hydroboration agents and the net result is the same. The mechanism of the oxidation is complex, but a proposed mechanism is provided in the Reaction Guide.

Notes

Because hydroboration places the B on the less substituted C and the B
is replaced by an OH in the oxidation, the **net result after both steps** is
formation of:

(A) Anti Markovnikov alcohol
                    ROH

Because hydroboration is syn- and OH replaces the B without a change
of stereochemistry of attachment, the H and OH in the alcohol are:

(B) syn addition

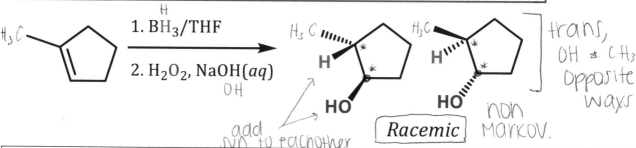

1. BH₃/THF

2. H₂O₂, NaOH(aq)
         OH

HO   HO

add syn to each other

Racemic   non Markov.

trans, OH ≠ CH₃ opposite ways

Notes

Ozonolysis differs from the other reactions of alkenes in that instead of *adding* atoms to the pi bond, **both bonds of the C=C are broken**. The first step of ozonolysis is to react the alkene with ozone (O_3):

The ozonide is exposed to either reducing or oxidizing workup:

(A) Reducing workup (Zn/H_3O^+ or R_2S):	(B) Oxidizing workup (H_2O_2)

Notes   Ozone = O_3

The net ozonolysis reactions that you see generally look like these:

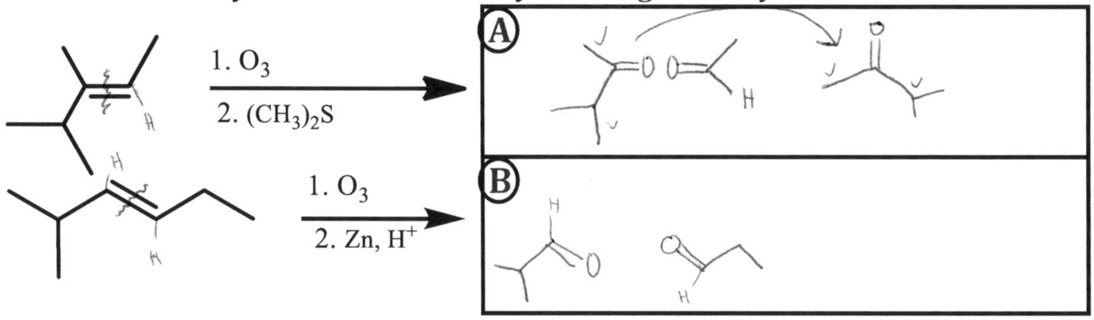

1. O_3
2. $(CH_3)_2S$

(A)

1. O_3
2. Zn, H^+

(B)

If there is more than one double bond, all will react:

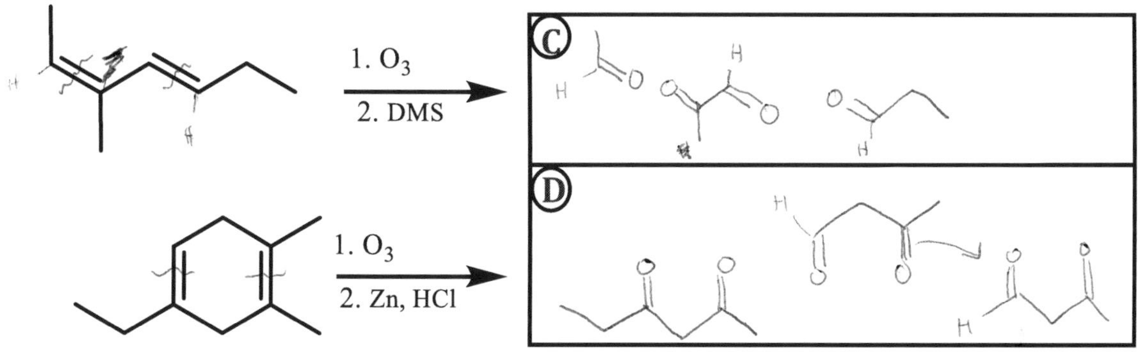

1. O_3
2. DMS

(C)

1. O_3
2. Zn, HCl

(D)

Notes

Organic Chemist Definition of oxidation and reduction:

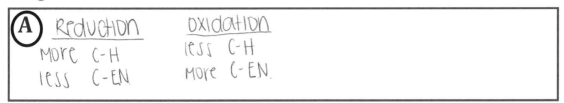

(A) Reduction   Oxidation
    more C-H   less C-H
    less C-EN   more C-EN.

Reaction of an alkene with osmium tetroxide (OsO_4) followed by a reductive workup leads to net *syn*-addition of two OH groups to the two carbons that were in the C=C bond:

OH, OH
1. OsO_4
2. H_2S or $NaHSO_4$

(B)   OH   OH   syn-

            concerted

An example where *syn*-addition would be evident:

(C)   achiral   →   chiral centers   OH   CH₃ + its enantiomer   OH

racemic
    mixture
    50% each
        product

Notes

Example. Fill in the major product of each reaction. Show stereochemistry where applicable.

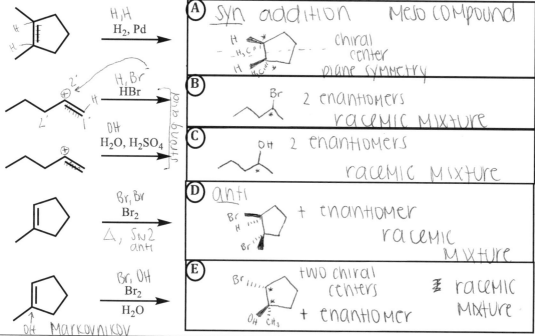

(A) syn addition   Meso compound
    chiral center
    plane symmetry

(B) Br   2 enantiomers
    racemic mixture

(C) OH   2 enantiomers
    racemic mixture

(D) anti   + enantiomer
    racemic mixture

(E) Br   two chiral centers   ≠ racemic mixture
    + enantiomer

Notes

LG X	subs, elimination
OH	activate subs, E1
(alkene)	addition

addition
1) what adds?
2) where do the groups add?
3) what direction do they point?
4) C⁺ rearrangement

$$\underset{}{\overset{H^{\oplus}}{\longrightarrow}}$$

Example. Fill in the major product of each reaction. Show stereochemistry where applicable.

strong acid

H_2SO_4, H_2O

A achiral molecule

1. $Hg(OAc)_2$, H_2O
2. $NaBH_4$

B OH R or S   50% S/R   MIX OF TWO
        50% S/S   diastereomers

concerted   MCPBA   opixidation

C not meso   + its enantiomer   racemic mixture

1. OsO_4 OH OH syn
2. DMS

D OH OH not meso   racemic mixture
     R R

1. O_3
2. Zn, HCl

E

Notes

234

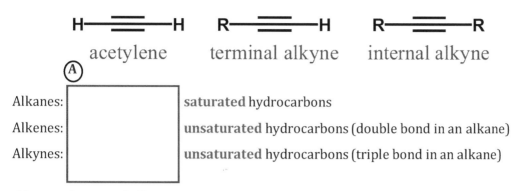

acetylene   terminal alkyne   internal alkyne

(A)

Alkanes: [   ]   **saturated** hydrocarbons

Alkenes: **unsaturated** hydrocarbons (double bond in an alkane)

Alkynes: **unsaturated** hydrocarbons (triple bond in an alkane)

Nomenclature of alkynes is much like that for alkanes, with modifications:

1. always designate the longest chain having

   (B) [   ]

2. Number the parent chain such that

   (C) [   ]

3. change the 'ane' ending of the name you would use if it were an alkane into an 'yne' ending to indicate that it has a triple bond in it.

Notes

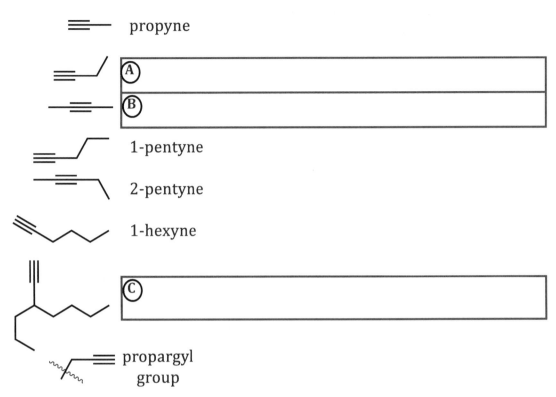

propyne

(A)

(B)

1-pentyne

2-pentyne

1-hexyne

(C)

propargyl
    group

NOTE: Because it is linear there are no E or Z isomers

Notes

4. If there is more than one triple bond, use a "-diyne", "-triyne", etc. at the end of the name in place of the "yne", with multiple numbers indicating where the triple bonds are (just like for alkenes):

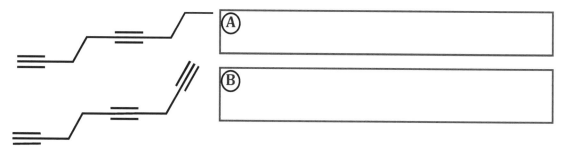

Ⓐ

Ⓑ

5. If alcohol functionalities are present in addition to alkyne:

Ⓒ

if both alkyne and alkene units are present, number the parent so that

Ⓓ

IF AND ONLY IF there is a tie between the two in term of numbering the parent, alkene > alkyne (the **lowest** number is given to the one that comes **first** alphabetically).

Notes

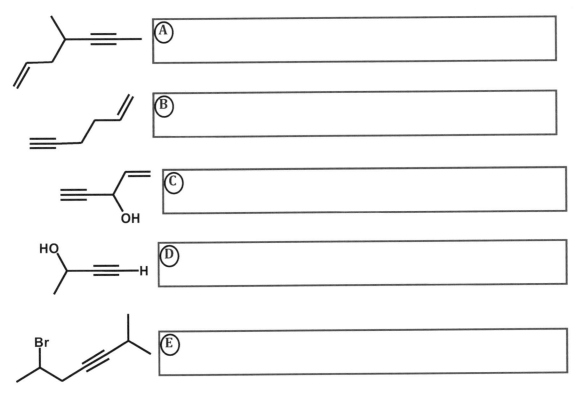

A

B

C

D

Br E

Note the order of the endings in example C: en-yn-ol

Notes

238

Alkynes can undergo many of the same reactions as alkenes by adding reagents across pi bonds. The alkyne unit has two pi bonds, so they can react once or twice to add across one or both of the alkyne pi bonds, following the same trends as we saw for alkenes. Consider hydrohalogenation:

Hydrohalogenation

Get rid of pi bond.
Add H (less subst. C)
Add X (more subt C)

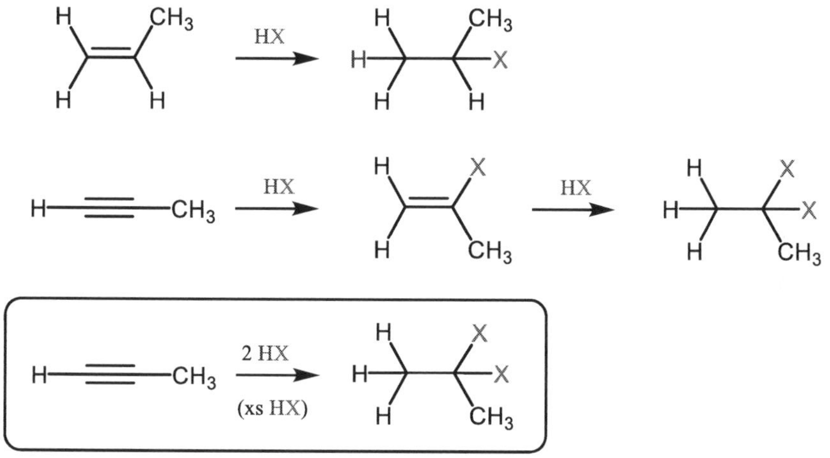

... and halogenation:

Halogenation

Get rid of pi bond.
Add X to each side,
anti- to each other

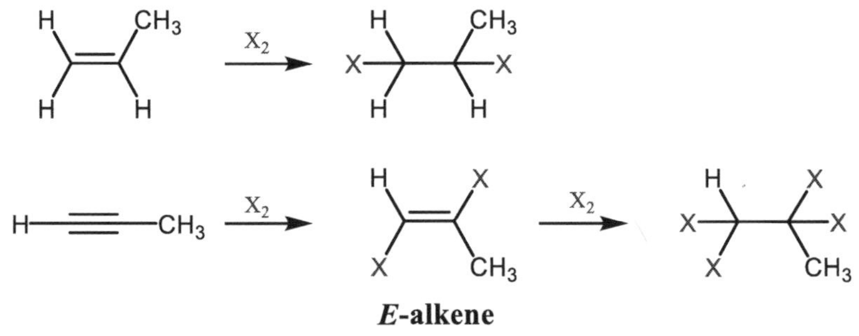

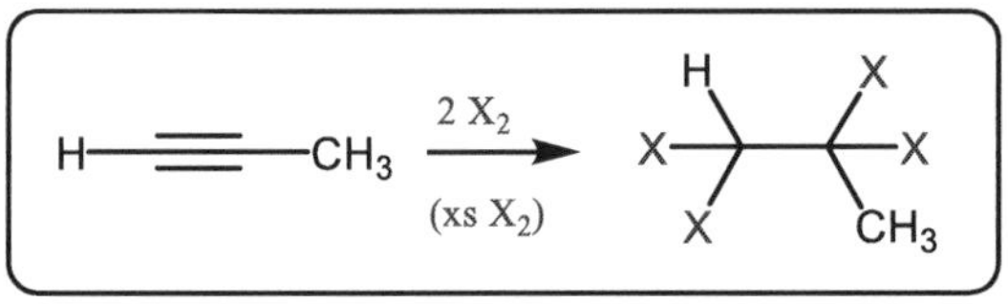

E-alkene

Notes

Alkynes can also be hydrogenated, either all the way to alkanes, by *syn*-addition of one equiv H_2, or by *anti*-addition of one equiv H_2 depending on the reagents:

Three ways to Add H!

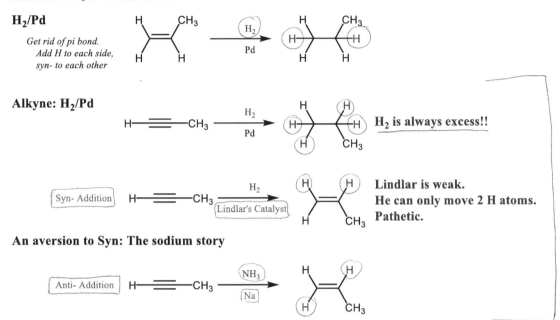

H₂/Pd

*Get rid of pi bond.
Add H to each side,
syn- to each other*

Alkyne: H₂/Pd

H₂ is always excess!!

Syn- Addition

**Lindlar is weak.
He can only move 2 H atoms.
Pathetic.**

An aversion to Syn: The sodium story

Anti- Addition

Notes

The biggest difference we will see between alkyne and alkene addition reactions is when we try to make an alcohol from an alkyne. It turns out that a double bond to the same C that has an –OH on it is often unstable and rearranges to a carbonyl (we will see why and how later):

Try to make an alcohol

Oxymercuration

Get rid of pi bond.
Add H to less subst side,
OH to more subst side

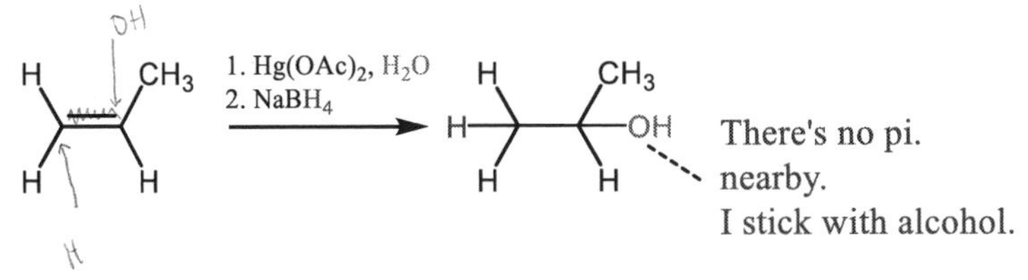

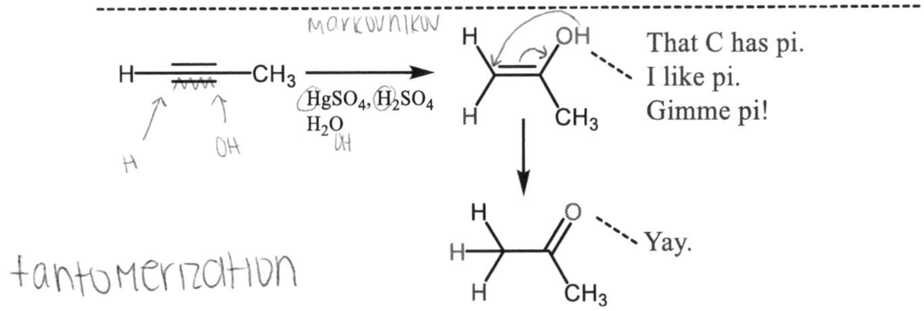

OH

H   CH₃   1. Hg(OAc)₂, H₂O   H   CH₃
                 2. NaBH₄   There's no pi.
H   H   H   OH   nearby.
                                    H   H   I stick with alcohol.
H

markovnikov   H   OH   That C has pi.
H——————CH₃   I like pi.
                HgSO₄, H₂SO₄   H   CH₃   Gimme pi!
                H₂O
H   OH   OH

                                H
tantomerization   H   O
                                H   CH₃   Yay.

Notes

HgSO₄
H₂O
R———≡———H ————→   OH   H   enol   [alkene
H₂SO₄   R   H   &
                                              alcohol]

O
R   H   More
H H   stable

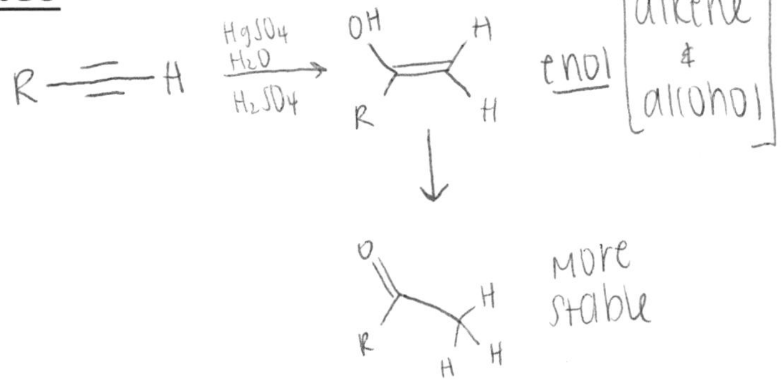

... This is the case whether we try to make a Markovnikov or a non-Markovnikov alcohol:

Try to make an alcohol

Hydroboration/Oxidation

Get rid of pi bond.
  Add H to more subst side,
  OH to less subst side

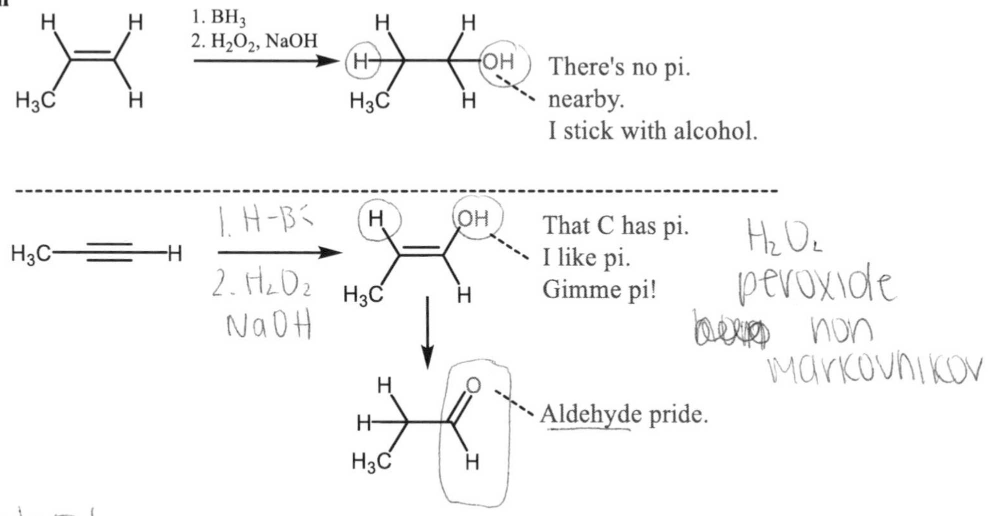

1. BH_3
2. H_2O_2, NaOH

There's no pi.
  nearby.
  I stick with alcohol.

H_3C———H

1. H-B'
2. H_2O_2
   NaOH

That C has pi.
  I like pi.
  Gimme pi!

H_2O_2
peroxide
~~but~~ non
       Markovnikov

Aldehyde pride.

alkyne → alcohol

Notes

Alkynes can be prepared by sequential elimination of two equiv HX from an alkyl dihalide via an E2 mechanism, in a manner analogous to that used to prepare alkenes:

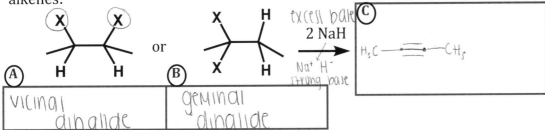

(A) vicinal dihalide   (B) geminal dihalide

excess base
2 NaH
Na⁺ H⁻ strong base

(C) $H_3C - \equiv - CH_3$

The second elimination is far more difficult, and the reaction can be stopped after one elimination:

$$\xrightarrow[E_2]{NaH}$$ (D) $$\xrightarrow[E_2]{NaH}$$ (E)

The reverse of double elimination is double addition ...

Notes

(NaNH₂)
$$\xrightarrow{Br_2} \xrightarrow{2NH}$$

Br   H
  ⌇ ⌇H
H₃C   Br

$$H_3C - \equiv - H$$

Addition reactions we studied for alkenes can work for alkynes

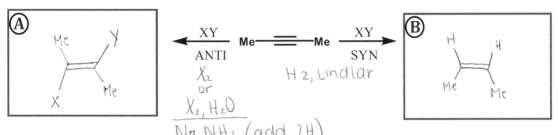

(A) ← XY / ANTI — Me≡Me — XY / SYN → (B)

X_2
or
X_2, H_2O
Na, NH_3 (add 2H)

We have TWO pi bonds in an alkyne unit:

H_3C≡CH_3 →X-X→ (A) →X-X→ (B)

Notes

≡ —1 Br_2→

enough —2 Br_2→
add to —Xs Br_2→
both
π bonds —H_2→ (always xs)

Alkynes can react with HX, yielding Markovnikov products. You should be able to deduce the mechanism in analogy to the reaction you know for alkenes. One equiv of HX leads to an alkene. Excess HX leads to the alkane.

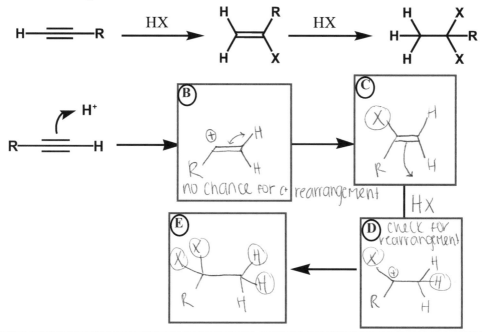

B no chance for c+ rearrangement

C

D check for rearrangement

HX

E

Notes

Alkynes react with halogens in analogy to alkenes. One or two halogen additions can take place across the unsaturated unit:

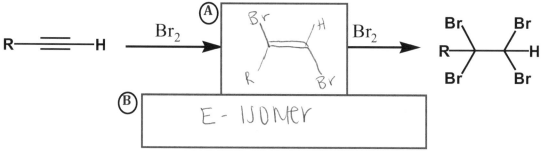

(B) E- ISOMer

Though the net result is what we saw for halogenation of alkenes, the mechanism is different:

(C)

Notes

MESO COMPOUND

An alkyne can be hydrogenated using conditions similar to those used
to hydrogenate an alkene (H_2/ transition metal catalyst):

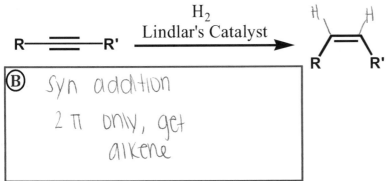

XS

$$R\!-\!\!\equiv\!\!-R' \xrightarrow[\text{Pt, Pd, Ni}]{H_2}$$

(A)

Gentler conditions (a less active catalyst) are required if conversion of an
Alkyne to an alkene is desired without further hydrogenation. To do this,
use H_2 with **Lindlar's catalyst** ($Pd/CaCO_3$, $Pb(OAc)_2$, quinoline).

$$R\!-\!\!\equiv\!\!-R' \xrightarrow[\text{Lindlar's Catalyst}]{H_2}$$

(B) syn addition

2 π only, get
alkene

Notes

syn ≠ cis

just direction
of things
you add

don't need
to draw H's

248

When an alkali metal such as Na or K is dissolved in liquid ammonia, solvated electrons are formed. The resulting solution can be used to reduce alkynes:

The mechanism is somewhat complex and involves radicals:

✳ do not memorize ✳

Notes

Tautomers:

Ⓐ easily interconverted constitutional isomers

Ⓑ enol

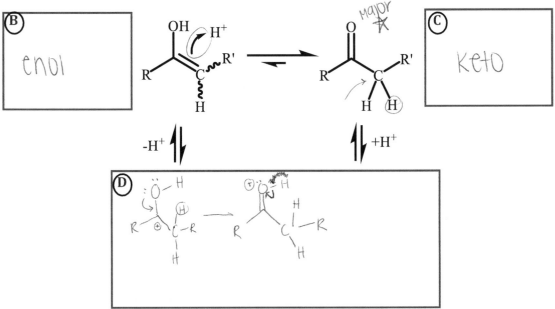

Ⓒ keto

Ⓓ

Notes

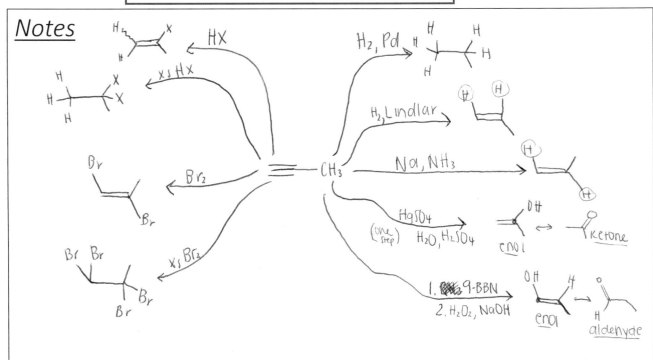

$H_3C-C\equiv C-CH_3$ $\xrightarrow[\text{2. etc}]{\text{1. 9BBN}}$ enol → ketone

$H-C\equiv C-H$ $\xrightarrow[\substack{H_2SO_4 \\ H_2O}]{HgSO_4}$ → aldehyde

Alkynes can undergo hydration reactions:

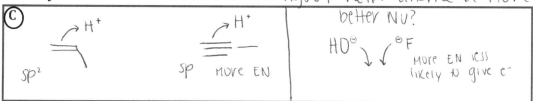

As with alkenes, hydration of an alkyne leads to initial formation of a Markovnikov alcohol. This tautomerizes, so the observed product will be a carbonyl.

Another difference from alkene hydration is that e need to add a mercury salt. This is needed because: HgSO4 helps alkyne be more reactwe

C

better NU?

H⁺

H⁺

SP²   SP   MOre EN

HO⊖ ⊖F
      MOre EN less
      likely to give e⁻

Notes

Alkynes can undergo hydroboration/oxidation:

R———H

1. R_2BH

2. H_2O_2, NaOH(aq)
non   OH

As with alkenes, hydroboration/oxidation of an alkyne leads to initial formation of a Non-Markovnikov alcohol. This tautomerizes, so the observed product will be a carbonyl.

The hydroboration/oxidation of a terminal alkyne leads to formation of an aldehyde:

enol

1. R_2BH

2. H_2O_2, NaOH(aq)

← remains unchanged

Notes	For alkenes & alkynes		
syn		anti	MIX
all		X_2	strong acid
others		↓	or
		Cl_2, Br_2, etc	"Hg"...

252

A **strong** base can deprotonate a terminal alkyne:

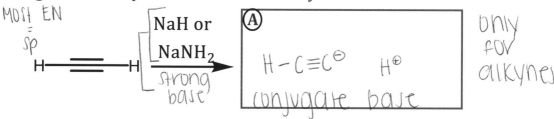

MOST EN
= SP

H———H

NaH or
NaNH₂
strong base

Ⓐ
H−C≡C⊖   H⊕
conjugate base

only for alkynes

The **acetylide anion** can then be used as a nucleophile in an S_N2 reaction:

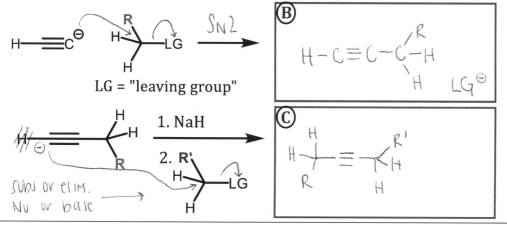

H——C⊖   R
         H⟩—LG S_N2
         H

LG = "leaving group"

Ⓑ
H−C≡C−C−H
         R
         H   LG⊖

1. NaH

2. R'
H—LG
H

subs or elim.
Nu or base

Ⓒ
H   R'
H—⟩=⟨—H
R   H

Notes

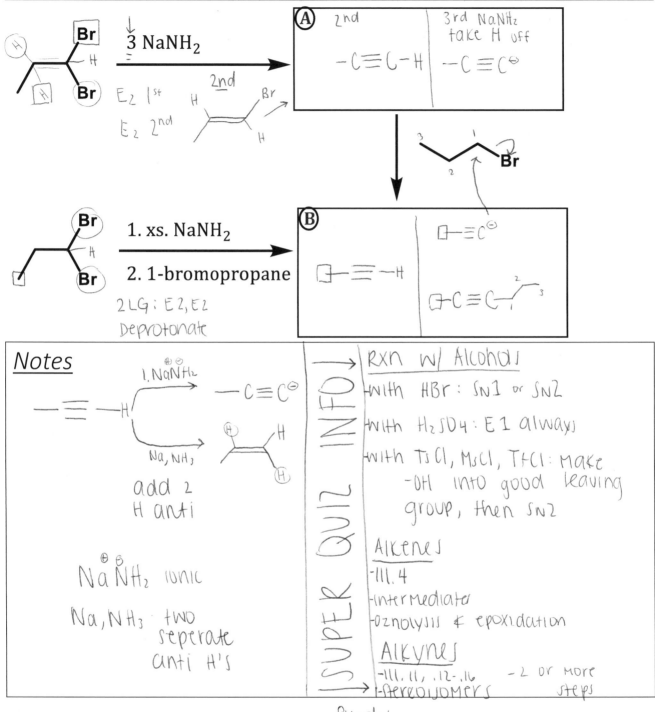

(A) 2nd | 3rd NaNH₂ take H off

$-C\equiv C-H$ | $-C\equiv C^{\ominus}$

3 NaNH₂

E₂ 1st
E₂ 2nd

2nd

(B)

1. xs. NaNH₂
2. 1-bromopropane

2LG: E2, E2
Deprotonate

$\square-\equiv-H$ | $\square-\equiv C^{\ominus}$

$\square-C\equiv C-$

Notes

1. NaNH₂

$-C\equiv C^{\ominus}$

Na, NH₃

add 2
H anti

$\overset{\ominus\ominus}{Na NH_2}$ ionic

Na, NH₃ two
seperate
anti H's

SUPER QUIZ INFO

Rxn w/ Alcohol
- with HBr: SN1 or SN2
- with H₂SO4: E1 always
- with TsCl, MsCl, TfCl: Make
  -OH into good leaving
  group, then SN2

Alkenes
- III.4
- intermediate
- oznolysis & epoxidation

Alkynes
- III.11, .12-.16   — 2 or more
- stereoisomers   steps

Study
Fall 2018 Exam 3

fall 2018 Exam 3
practice set

(A) **Observation** | 7 electrons in valence shell |

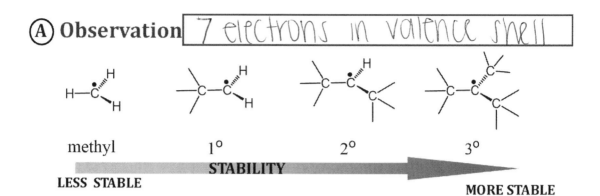

methyl   1°   2°   3°

STABILITY

LESS STABLE   MORE STABLE

(B) **Explanation**

hyperconjugation

Notes

Resonance Stabilizes Carbon-Centered Radicals

Secondary | Primary with resonance | Tertiary | Secondary with resonance | Tertiary with resonance

STABILITY →

LESS STABLE   **MORE STABLE**

Notes   Resonance very stabilizing for radicals

Peroxide-initiated hydrobromination
is an alternative way to add H and Br

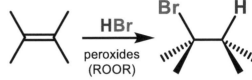

HBr
peroxides
(ROOR)

(A) Initiation

RO—OR $\xrightarrow{heat}$ 2·OR

Br–H ⤳ OR ⟶ Br· + HOR

Initiation:
forming
 radicals

(B) Propagation

radical: add
to π bond
or
abstract a H

1. Br· ⤳ ⟶ Br⟶·

propogation:
 chain
 reaction

2. Br⟶· ⤳ H—Br ⟶ Br⟶H + Br·

(C) Net Reaction

⟶ + H–Br ⟶ Br⟶H

Add up prop-
agation steps,
cancel as possible

Notes

257

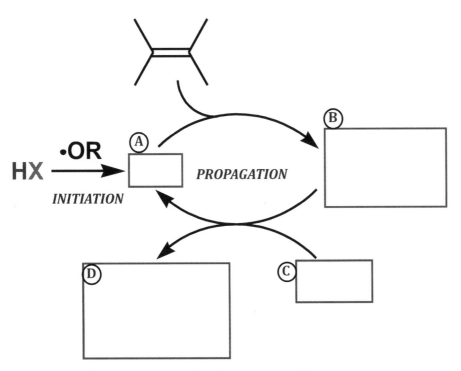

HX $\xrightarrow[\textbf{\textit{INITIATION}}]{\bullet OR}$ (A)   *PROPAGATION*   (B)

(D)   (C)

Termination occurs when any two radicals come together:

(E)

Notes

Lecture Topic III.17: Radicals I
Peroxide-Mediated Hydrobromination

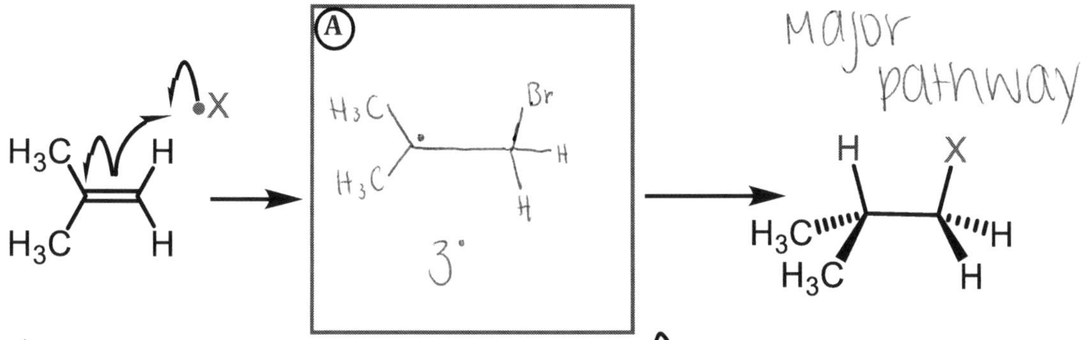
A
3°
Major pathway

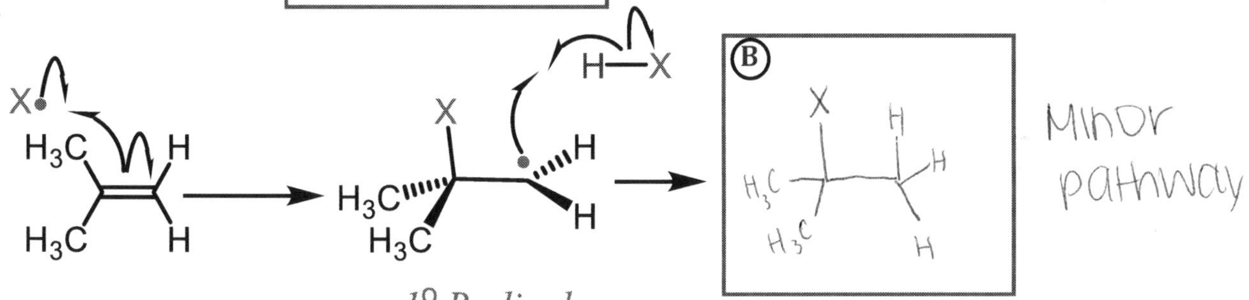
B
Minor pathway

1° Radical

Once again, the major product is that derived from the more stable intermediate, in this case the more substituted radical that picks up the H atom, so we get: (C) anti-Markovnikov product

Notes

Note that the peroxide-mediated (radical intermediate) hydrohalogenation yields the so-called "anti-Markovnikov" product, while the peroxide-free hydrohalogenation (carbocation intermediate) yields the Markivnikov product. This gives a researcher access to whichever product is desired:

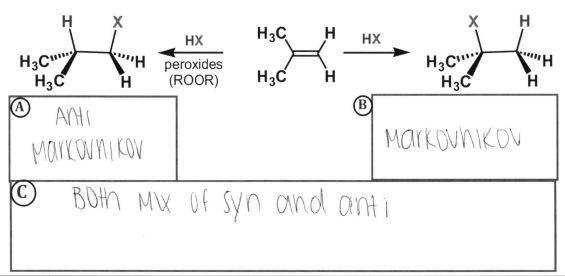

(A) Anti Markovnikov

(B) Markovnikov

(C) Both Mix of syn and anti

Notes

Lecture Topic III.18: Radicals II
Radical Halogenation of Alkanes

Alkyl halides can also be prepared from alkanes. Alkanes do not have very polar bonds, and do not readily react with common acids or bases. If we generate a very reactive species, like a **radical** we can observe reactions of alkanes. A good way to generate a halide radical is by excitation of X_2 with light.

$$R\text{–}H + X_2 \xrightarrow[\text{(light)}]{h\nu} R\text{–}X + HX$$

replace H with Cl or Br

The dihalides have different reactivities towards radical formation, so only **Cl_2 and Br_2** are commonly used in the above reaction:

$$I_2 < \boxed{Br_2 < Cl_2 <} F_2$$

REACTIVITY →

Because we are using such reactive species (radicals) it is often difficult to control these reaction to yield a single product, as we will see ...

Notes

We can write the discrete steps of the radical chain mechanism:

(A) **Initiation**

$$Cl_2 \xrightarrow{h\nu} 2Cl\cdot$$

(B) **Propagation**

$$Cl\cdot + CH_4 \longrightarrow HCl + CH_3\cdot \text{ (Methyl radical)}$$
$$CH_3\cdot + Cl_2 \longrightarrow CH_3Cl + Cl\cdot$$

(C) **Net Reaction**

$$CH_4 + Cl_2 \longrightarrow CH_3Cl + HCl$$

(D) **Termination**
   Minor
   products

$$Cl\cdot + Cl\cdot \longrightarrow Cl_2$$
$$CH_3\cdot + CH_3\cdot \longrightarrow CH_3-CH_3$$
$$CH_3\cdot + Cl\cdot \longrightarrow CH_3Cl$$

Notes

Termination: any time 2 radicals combine

... or we can write a simple cycle (shows **initiation** and **propagation** but not **termination**):

$$CH_4$$

$$\frac{1}{2} \ Cl_2 \xrightarrow{\ h\nu\ } \textcircled{A} \quad \textit{PROPAGATION} \quad \textcircled{C}$$

$$\textit{INITIATION}$$

$$CH_3Cl$$

$$\textcircled{B} \qquad \textcircled{D}$$

Termination occurs when any two radicals come together.

Notes

263

Only Cl_2 and Br_2 are commonly used in this radical chain reaction because fluorine is too reactive and iodine is not reactive enough. The structure of the alkane we use also plays an important role.

The key step is the homolytic cleavage of the alkane C-H bond to form the radical:

   R–H $\rightarrow$ R• + H• ΔH = BDE (**bond dissociation enthalpy**)

BDE Trends:

Easier radical formation

Structure	BDE	
CH_3—H	104 kcal	
CH_3CH_2—H	98 kcal	
$CH_3CH_2CH_2$—H	98 kcal	(1º)
$(CH_3)_2CH$—H	95 kcal	(2º)
$(CH_3)_3C$—H	91 kcal	(3º)

The take-home lesson is:

Ⓐ  The more substituted radical the more stable

Notes

add Cl to most substituted carbon C w/ H

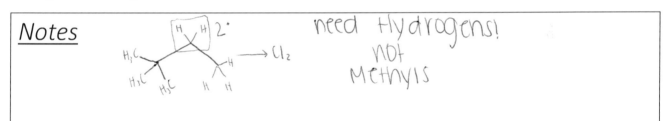

there are 2 secondary H atoms

there are 6 primary H atoms

Experimentally observed:		43%	57%
Statistically anticipated:		75%	25%

We observe a greater than statistically anticipated reactivity at the secondary site. The reaction has a greater **regioselectivity** for this site.

We already know that the secondary radical is more stable than the primary, and that the secondary C-H bond has a lower BDE, so this regioselectivity makes sense.

Notes

need Hydrogens!
not
Methyls

265

When Cl_2 is used, the relative reactivity can be approximated as:

Relative Reactivity of C–H:

3°	2°	1°
5.2	3.9	1

Use this to predict product distribution for the chlorination of propane:

there are 2 secondary H atoms

there are 6 primary H atoms

Rel. amount of 1° product = reactivity of 1° H x number of 1° H's
Rel. amount of 2° product = reactivity of 2° H x number of 2° H's

$$= 3.9 \times 2 = 7.8 = 43\% \text{ primary}$$
$$= 1 \times 6 = 6 = 57\% \text{ secondary}$$

Notes

Lecture Topic III.18: Radicals II
Radical Halogenation of Alkanes

Bromine is less reactive and therefore more **selective** than chlorine. Consider the observed products for these reactions:

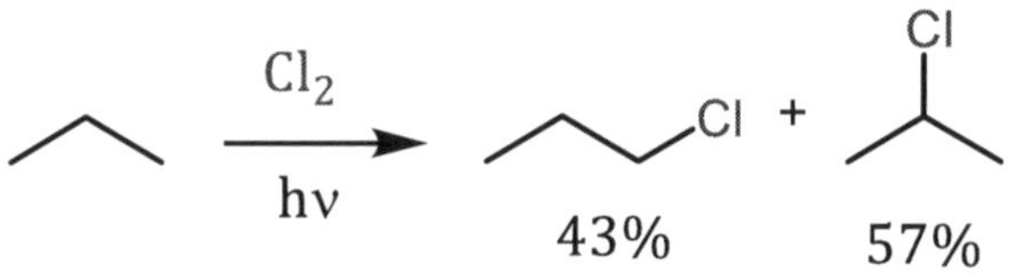

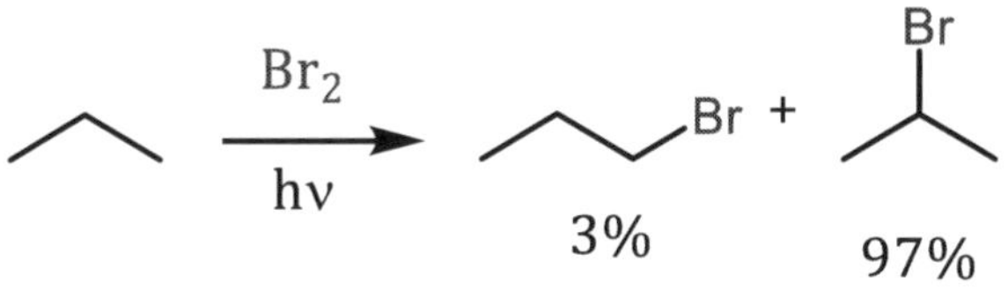

From these data we can deduce that the selectivity of bromine must be more pronounced than for chlorine. This is the case:

Site:	3°	2°	1°
Relative reactivity:	1640	82	1

Notes

↑ reactivity = ↓ selectivity

Alkenes can be used as starting materials to make **polymers**.

POLYMER: long molecule w/ same unit repeating

MONOMER: starting material to make polymer

REPEAT UNIT: piece that repeats in the polymer chain

EXAMPLE: $H_2C=CH_2 \longrightarrow$ repeat unit
    monomer $\uparrow$
                            how many
                              units
                            in chain

Notes

Radical Polymerization of an alkene:

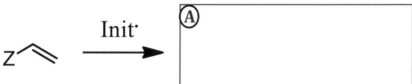

Mechanism of Polymer chain growth:

Unlike the other radical reactions of alkenes that we have seen, there is ONLY an initiator added to the alkene, no other reagents. A common radical initiator is Benzoyl Peroxide, $(PhC(O)O)_2$

Notes

Cationic Polymerization of an alkene:

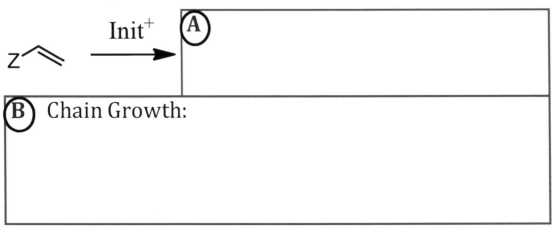

$$\text{Init}^+ \quad \text{(A)}$$

(B) Chain Growth:

Lewis acids can be good initiators for a cationic polymerization:

(C)

Notes

Anionic Polymerization of an alkene:

Z $\diagdown\diagup\diagup$ $\xrightarrow{\text{Init}^-}$ (A)

(B) Chain Growth:

You may notice that in the other reactions of alkenes, a cation or radical was the key intermediate. This is because it is more difficult to generate a carbanion. In order to do a successful anionic polymerization, **the group Z must**:

(C)

Notes

271

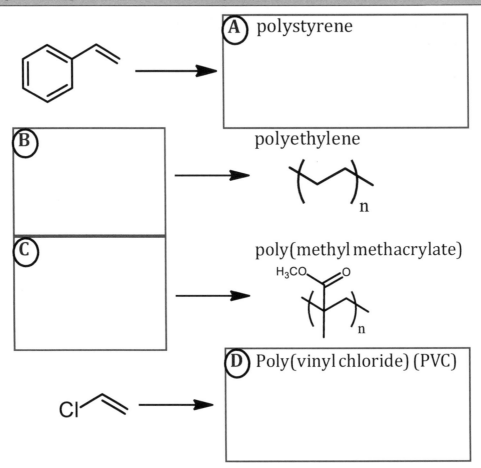

(A) polystyrene

polyethylene

(B)

(C)

poly(methyl methacrylate)

(D) Poly(vinyl chloride) (PVC)

Notes

272

Different energies of light elicit different changes in molecules that absorb them. In this course, we will consider UV, visible, IR and radio frequency radiation:

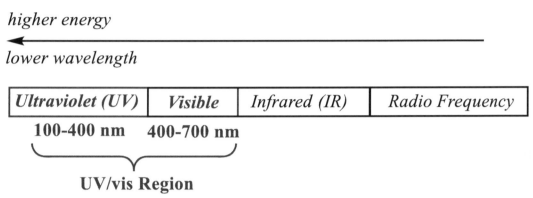

First, we will focus on how UV and visible light, collectively abbreviated UV–visible (UV/vis) light, interact with organic molecules. The UV/vis part of the spectrum we will consider spans a wavelength range from ~100–700 nm.

Notes

When a molecule absorbs UV/vis radiation of an appropriate energy, it causes one of the electrons to undergo an **electronic transition** from the highest occupied molecular orbital (HOMO) to the lowest unoccupied molecular orbital (LUMO).

An electron in a σ-bond gets promoted to a **σ-antibonding (σ*) orbital**:

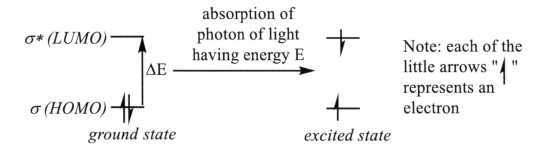

Note: each of the little arrows " ↑ " represents an electron

An electron in a π-bond gets promoted to a **π-antibonding (π*) orbital**:

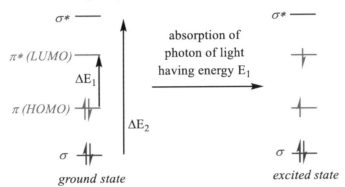

ground state　　　　　　　　　　　　　　*excited state*

Compared to the σ→ σ* transition, the π→ π* is:

Furthermore, the longer the π conjugated system, the lower the energy of the photon needed to promote the π→π* transition.

Notes

A UV-vis spectrometer is set up as follows:

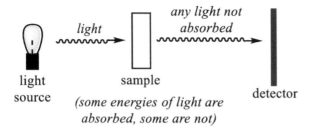

light source — light — sample — any light not absorbed — detector
(some energies of light are absorbed, some are not)

The spectrum is a plot of absorbance versus wavelength:

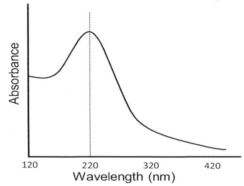

Notes

Lecture Topic VII.2. UV-vis Spectroscopy
Beer-Lambert Law and the molar extinction coefficient

The amount of light absorbed per mole of a sample is called the **molar absorptivity** or **molar extinction coefficient**.

The **Beer-Lambert Law** provides an equation relating the absorbance (A), pathlength (b), concentration (c) and extinction coefficient (ε):

For a constant pathlength, then, it is easy to monitor concentration, and thus to follow the reaction rate. If a species we are following gives spectrum **A** (absorbing at 220 nm) at the start of a reaction, and spectrum **B** after 1 h, we know that half of the compound is consumed in that one hour, because the absorption is halved.

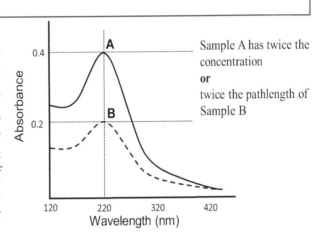

Sample A has twice the concentration

or

twice the pathlength of Sample B

Notes

Molecules absorb energy:

(A)

Leading to:

(B)

Expressing energy: $E = h\upsilon = \dfrac{hc}{\lambda}$

wavenumber ($\tilde{\upsilon}$):

(C)

Larger wavenumbers =

(D)

Notes

Bonds can vibrate in different ways, and each of these **vibrational modes** requires a different energy:

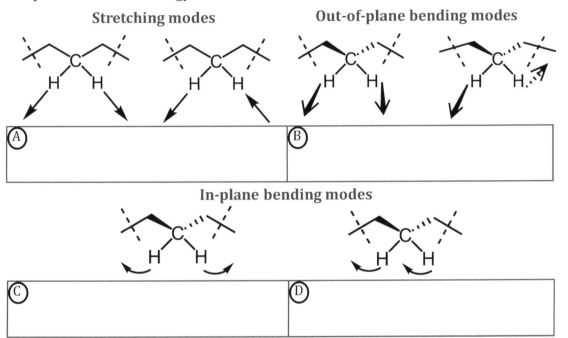

Stretching modes

Out-of-plane bending modes

Ⓐ

Ⓑ

In-plane bending modes

Ⓒ

Ⓓ

<u>Notes</u>

279

A typical IR spectrum has this appearance:

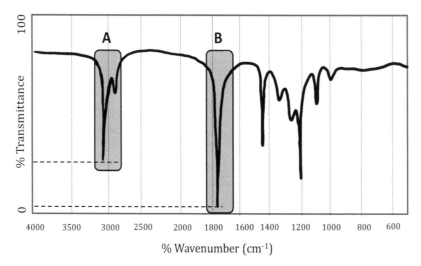

Band **A** corresponds to a set of bonds that absorbs ~75% of the IR light at 3000 cm^{-1} emitted by the source (i.e., 25% transmittance), whereas band **B** corresponds to a set of bonds that absorbs nearly 95% of the IR light at 1750 cm^{-1} (i.e., 5% transmittance).

Notes

280

Each type of bond has a characteristic energy of absorption for IR radiation:

Bond	Energy (cm^{-1})	Intensity
N≡C	2255-2220	m-s
C≡C	2260-2100	w-m
C=C	1675-1660	m
N=C	1650-1550	m
⬡ {	1600 **AND**	w-s
	1500-1425	
C=O	1775-1650	s
C—O	1250-1000	s
C—N	1230-1000	m
O—H	3650-3200	s (br)
O—H	3300-2500	s (br)
N—H	3500-3300	m (br)
C—H	3300-2725	m

C-H Bond (Stretch) Energy (cm^{-1})

C≡C—H	3300-ish
C=C—H	3100-3000
C—C—H	2950-2850

2820-ish and 2720-ish

C-H Bond (Bending)

—CH$_3$
—CH$_2$—   H
                —C—   } 1450-1400
                 |

980-960 trans

730-670 cis

840-800 trisubstituted

990 and 910 monosubstituted

890 disubstituted terminal

There are several points worth noting:

Stronger bonds:

Ⓐ

More polar bonds:

Ⓑ

Resonance influences bond order, and therefore bonds strength:

Resonance Contributors   Resonance Hybrid

$C=O$
bond order = 2

$C=O$
bond order = 1

Ⓒ

Amides have lower-energy C=O stretches than ketones

Notes

Lecture Topic VII.4. Infrared Spectroscopy
IR decision tree

If there an aromatic ring?
Must have all of these:
C–H (~3050 cm^{-1})
C=C ~1600 and ~1500 cm^{-1}
Overtone 1680-2000 cm^{-1}

↓ **No**

C=O? (1650-1850 cm^{-1})

If yes, consider aldehyde, ketone, carboxylic acid, amide, anhydride, acid chloride

↓ FGs without the band include: Alkane, alkene, alkyne, alcohol, amine, nitro, nitrile

Band > ~3100 cm^{-1}?

If so, could be:
alcohol, amine, alkene, terminal alkyne

If not, could be internal alkyne, nitrile, Ether, nitro, alkane

~3050 cm^{-1} (possibly as shoulder) alkene- **and** C=C at ~1650 cm^{-1}

Sharp (~3300-3100 cm^{-1}) terminal alkyne

U-shape = alcohol

V-shape = 2° amine

W-shape = 1° amine

Weak 2100-2200 cm^{-1} internal alkyne

Strong 2200 cm^{-1} Nitrile

strong 1000-1200 cm^{-1} ether

1350 **and** 1550 cm^{-1} nitro

Alkane – none of the above

U-shape = COOH

V-shape = amide C(O)NHR

W-shape = amide C(O)NH$_2$

FG's with this band: consider –COOH or amide

Strong Band > ~3100 cm^{-1}?

Functional groups without this band: consider aldehyde, ketone, anhydride, acid chloride

(Often) Clefted C=O **and** C-Cl at 600-800 Acid chloride

Double peak 2720/2820 cm^{-1} aldehyde

C-O strong 1000-1200 cm^{-1} ester

Two C=O bands **and** C-O 1000-1200 cm^{-1} anhydride

Only one C=O, no others of above: ketone

Notes

283

IR Spectrum for Hexanal

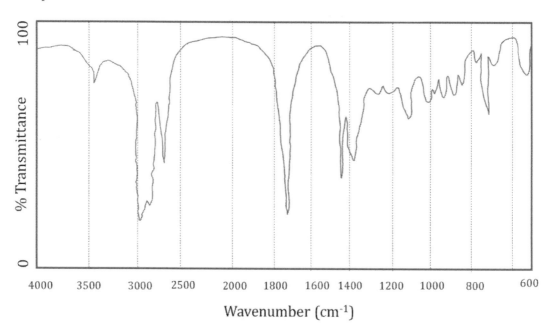

Notes

IR Spectrum for cyclohexene

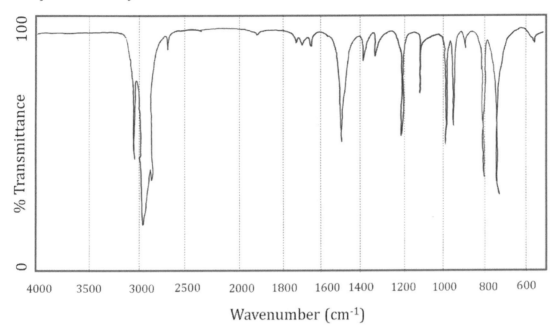

Notes

IR Spectrum for nitrohexane

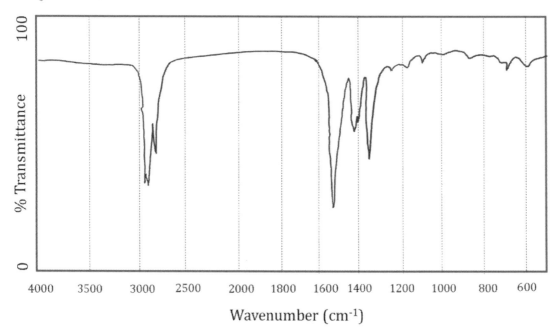

Notes

IR Spectrum for 1-hexyne

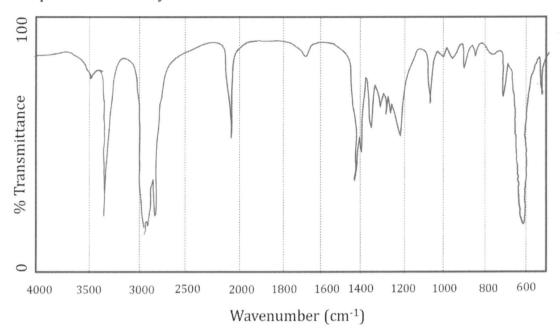

Notes

IR Spectrum for 2-butyne

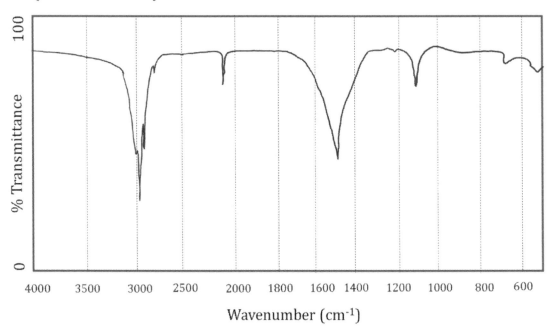

Notes

IR Spectrum for 3-octanol

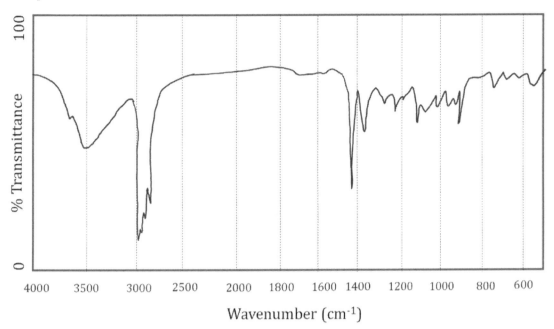

Notes

IR Spectrum for diethylamine

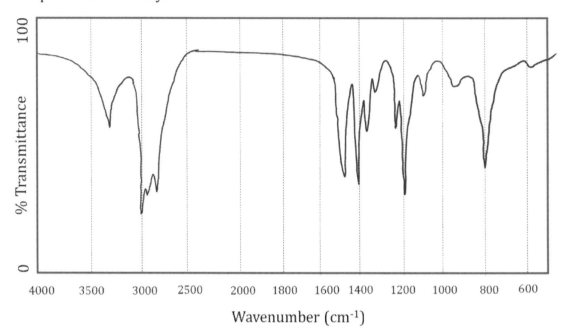

Notes

IR Spectrum for hexylamine

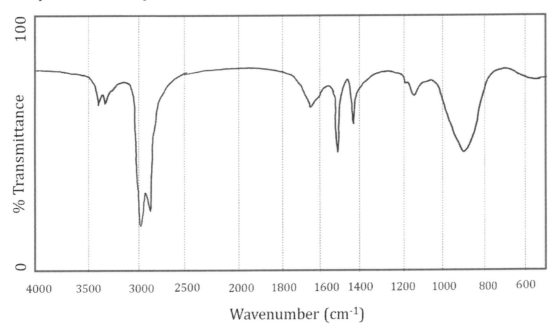

Notes

IR Spectrum for acetonitrile (CH_3CN)

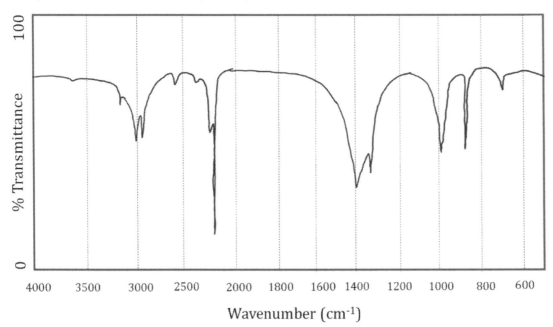

Wavenumber (cm^{-1})

Notes

IR Spectrum for diethylether

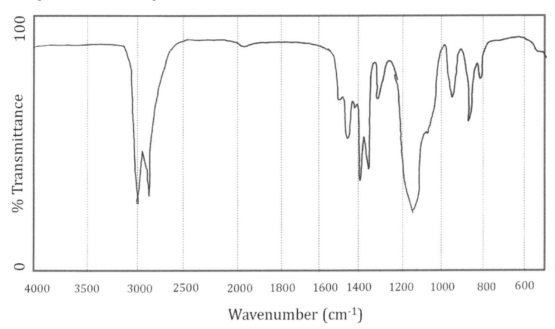

Notes

IR Spectrum for hexanoic acid

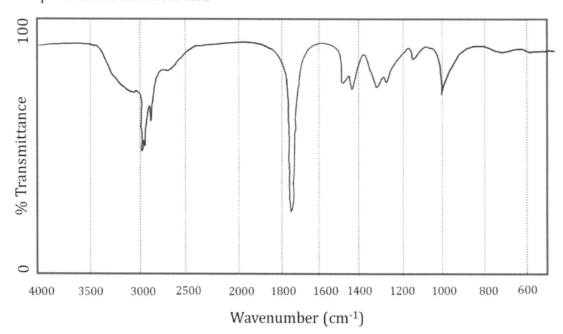

Notes

IR Spectrum for *N*-methylacetamide $(CH_3C(O)N(H)CH_3)$

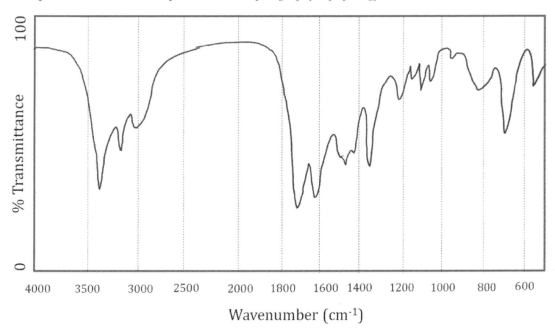

Wavenumber (cm^{-1})

Notes

IR Spectrum for propamide ($CH_3CH_2C(O)NH_2$)

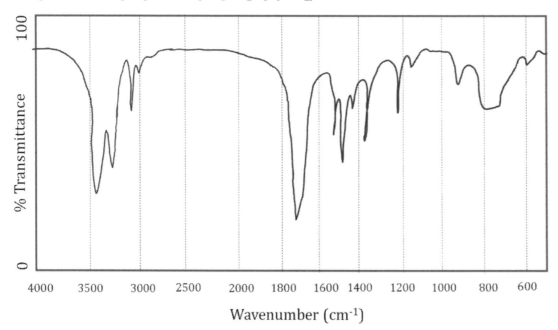

Wavenumber (cm^{-1})

Notes

IR Spectrum for propanoyl chloride

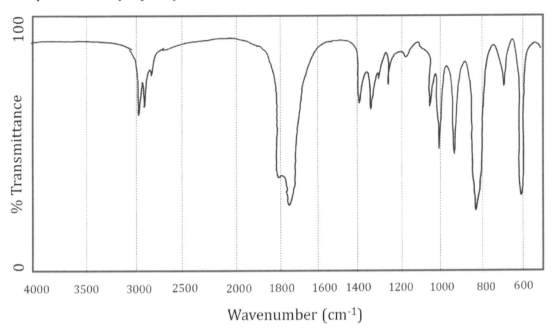

Notes

IR Spectrum for acetic anhydride

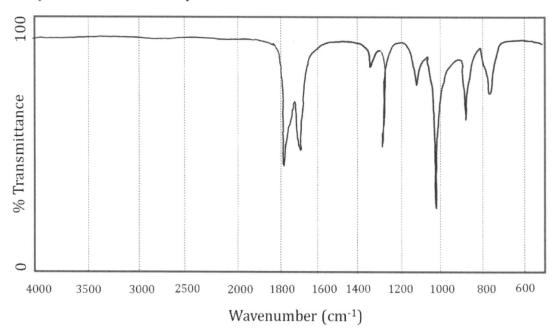

Notes

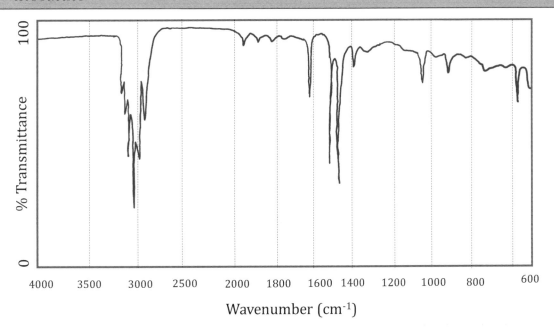

Notes

Lecture Topic VII.5. Introduction to Nuclear Magnetic Resonance
NMR active nuclei

NMR stands for:

(A)

NMR spectroscopy is a technique that is used to identify compounds.
A NMR Spectrum is a plot of

(B)

vs.

(C)

Many common nuclei are NMR active, including:

(D)

In this Lecture Guide, we will focus on ^{13}C and ^{1}H NMR spectrometry

Notes

A representative spectrum is shown here:

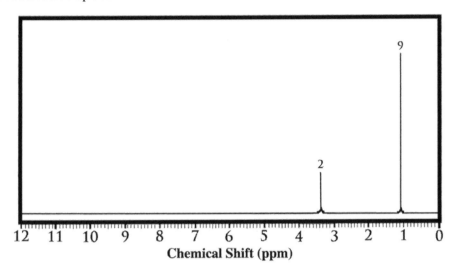

The energy at which we observe a peak can tell us

thus aiding in the compound's identification.

Notes

301

Nuclei are charged. Charged particles interact with magnetic fields. A 'resonating' nucleus generates a magnetic field of its own. This generated magnetic field may be aligned with or oppose the applied field. It takes more energy to oppose the applied field.

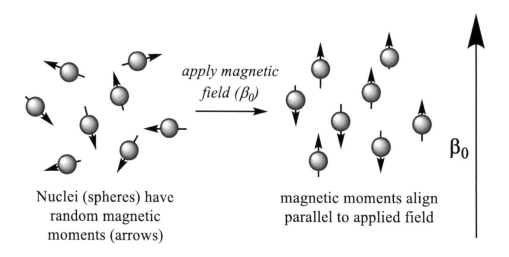

<table>
<tr><td>Nuclei (spheres) have random magnetic moments (arrows)</td><td>magnetic moments align parallel to applied field</td></tr>
</table>

Nuclei (spheres) have
random magnetic
moments (arrows)

apply magnetic field (β_0)

magnetic moments align
parallel to applied field

β_0

Notes

One can add energy to get the nucleus' magnetic field to 'flip' direction. By measuring the energy needed to accomplish this flip, we generate a NMR spectrum:

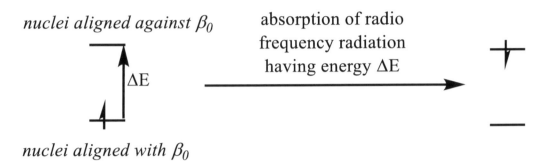

nuclei aligned against β_0

ΔE

absorption of radio frequency radiation having energy ΔE

nuclei aligned with β_0

Notes

303

Lecture Topic VII.5. Introduction to Nuclear Magnetic Resonance
Magnetically equivalent nuclei

Each set of **magnetically equivalent** nuclei absorb a certain energy of photon. Free rotation about single bonds averages the signal, so that nuclei that can be interconverted by single bond rotation are equivalent. Consider how many types of H nuclei are in each of these molecules:

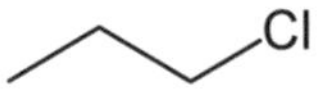

A)

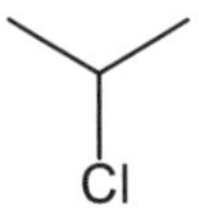

B)

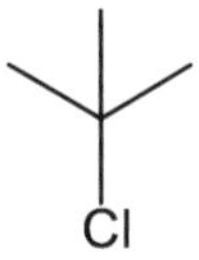

C)

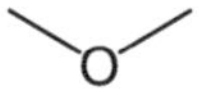

D)

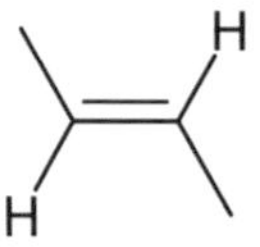

E)

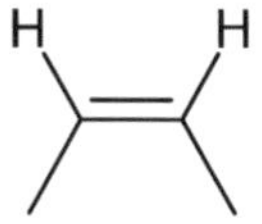

F)

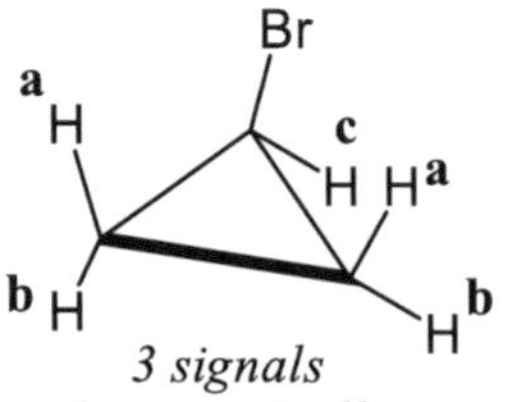

3 signals
3 magnetically inequivalent proton sets

Notes

Nuclei in molecules have electrons around them. Since electrons are oppositely charged compared to nuclei, they exert an opposing effect on the applied magnetic field. More electron density thus **shields** a nucleus and lowers the energy needed to flip it. In this way, NMR is an indirect way to measure electron density, which allows us to deduce the type of group containing the nucleus.

Protons in Electron Poor environment:

Ⓐ

Protons in Electron Rich environment:

Ⓑ

← Frequency increases

δ **Increases**

Higher number on x axis in spectrum

Notes

The area under each signal in an NMR spectrum is proportional to the number of nuclei giving the signal. The area under the peak is called the **integration.**

The integrations are printed above the peaks in this book. Consider this ^{1}H NMR spectrum:

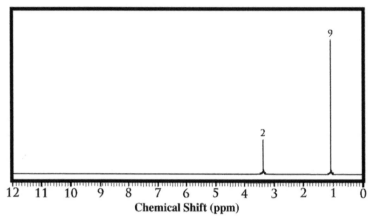

The ratio of peaks is 2:9. This could mean that one peak is attributable to 2 H nuclei and the other is attributable to 9, or one to 4 H and one to 9 H; we only know the ratio.

Notes

If there is an NMR active nucleus (i.e., one which resonates thus creating a magnetic field) near another NMR-active nucleus, the two will influence each other. Depending on the direction of nucleus **A**'s magnetic field, nucleus **A** may shield or reinforce the magnetic field experienced by its neighboring nucleus **B**:

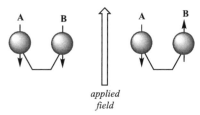

applied field

This causes the signal for nucleus **A** to split slightly into two peaks. The shape of the peak will be:

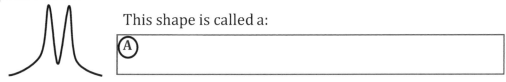

This shape is called a:

Ⓐ

As there are more and more NMR-active nuclei adjacent to nucleus **A**, the splitting gets more elaborate ...

Notes

For 1H NMR, the **multiplicity** (m, the number of smaller peaks into which the signal is split) is equal to $n+1$, where n is the number of H on neighbor C:

#H on neighbor C:	Type of peak		Ratio of heights
	singlet		1
	doublet		1:1
	triplet		1:2:1
	quartet		1:3:3:1
	quintet		1:4:6:4:1
	sextet		1:5:10:10:5:1
	septet		1:6:15:20:15:6:1

Notes

General trends in ^{13}C NMR shifts are provided here:

Carbon (Shown)	Chemical Shift		Carbon (Shown)	Chemical Shift	
$Si(CH_3)_4$	0		O—C	50-80	
—CH_3	10-35		N—C	40-60	
—CH_2—	15-50		C—X	X = I	0-35
—C(H)—	20-60			X = Br	20-65
				X = Cl	35-80
—C—	30-40				
=C<	100-150		C(=O)—Y	Y = H	190-200
				R	200-220
				OR	160-180
				OH	175-185
benzene—H	110-175			NR_2	165-175
≡C—	60-85				

Notes

Index

311